Hot Chocolate for your Soul

Discover Mindful Eating and Stop Dieting

By Jeni MacNab

JMAC

The information in this book is not intended as medical advice, diagnosis or treatment. If you have any medical condition it is advised to seek advice from a fully qualified physician.

A catalogue record of this title is available from the British Library

ISBN 978-0-9565508-0-4

Published by Jeni MacNab

Printed and bound in the UK by Self Publishing Direct Keele University Staffordshire ST5 5BG

About the author

Jeni MacNab has a wealth of experience to offer on many different areas of health and wellness. Jeni has worked in healthcare ove 30 years as a nurse, therapist, trainer, health promotion specialist, and workshop leader and has a number of qualifications to support this including a BSc in Health, RGN ONC, Counselling Skills Certificate, Meridian Energy Therapies Certificate, Aromatherapy Diploma, Kinesiology Certificate and Massage in Schools Certificate. Her beliefs and values around health and personal development are firmly rooted in her desire to support and encourage people becoming more self-aware. For Jeni this involves enabling, empowering and helping people change their beliefs and behaviours and understanding the mind-body connection. Her passion and expertise lies in personal development. She addresses this in a number of different ways using one-to one consultations, workshop and seminar presentations and Quiet Room Consultancy Services.

Acknowledgements

I would like to thank every person who has contributed to my life and has encouraged, inspired and touched me with their presence.

I will be eternally grateful to the people for their support and contributions to the creation of this book and for sharing their stories, thoughts and often their innermost feelings: Thank-You.

A great big thank-you to everyone who had the patience to read my book and offer me very useful and constructive feedback: David Sime, Claire McKenzie, Wendy Merrett, Wendy Birse, Ken Paterson, Eleanor Walker, Rachael Eves, Keni Wills and Kay Strang.

This book would not have been possible had it not been for my parents who I love dearly and the experiences I had throughout my life. Painful though they were at times I am grateful for the opportunities I was given and the learning and growth that developed as a result. I am very grateful to all my friends and siblings for their support and encouragement along the way. I would also like to show my gratitude and appreciation to all the authors of the many books I have read over the last 20 years and for their teachings which have inspired and empowered me to bring about positive change in my life. Finally I would like to thank my best friend Linda MacKay for her patience, her understanding and for always being there for me through the rough and smooth of my life's journey.

Contents

Introduction

Introduction

Perhaps the reason you have picked up this book is because of the pain and suffering you continue to put yourself through on a daily basis. Not expressing how you feel and using food to give you that temporary instant relief while pushing your feelings and emotions further and further down, or by denying yourself the true pleasure of eating without restriction.

Do you long to be able to eat without restriction, without the feeling of guilt and shame, do you long to be able to get back to "normal" eating, eating what you want, when you want and eating until you feel physically satisfied and full? If this is something you really long for, and never ever want to follow another diet again, then read on.

If you are happy with your relationship with food then perhaps you may not want to read this book, but rest assured if you have any imbalances in your body that affect your health then the chances are that many of them will have originated in the mind through your thoughts or beliefs.

Dieting only seeks to address the symptoms such as weight gain, weight loss, bingeing, cravings etc and not the cause which is usually always connected to how we feel. Dieting is restrictive and unsustainable and often leaves us feeling guilty and disappointed that we have failed. Unless we begin to address the cause then the symptoms will always remain. How to change your relationship with food using a more mindful approach may well surprise you, if you have been controlling your weight throughout your life in an attempt to suppress or deny your real needs or feelings.

The intention in writing this book is to help you understand what lies behind your unhealthy relationship with food and create the opportunity to change it. It will guide you through a very powerful process offering some simple but life changing strategies. It will show you how easily you can transform your relationship with food.

You will learn how to get in touch with your feelings and listen to your body and how it communicates with you. You will learn how to trust yourself and know what to eat, when to eat and how much to eat. You will begin to recognize what eating triggers you have and how you can easily and effortlessly overcome these. Finally you will understand how to balance eating for health with eating for pleasure without any form of deprivation or guilt.

<u>MY STORY ......THEN</u>

My story is not just about my relationship with food, I think it is probably more about my struggle to try and understand myself and what has driven me to behave the way I have at different times throughout my life. It is also about the self-realisation that comes through this understanding.

My older sister was put on a diet when she was around 14yrs old. When my mum told her she was too fat and that she would have to go on a diet, I asked if I also had to go on a diet. Fortunately for me my mum didn't think I was too fat at that point, so I felt quite smug that I was an acceptable weight and my sister wasn't. (Again within our family we were encouraged to compete with our siblings, as this resulted in parental approval on many occasions).

This was to be the first of many diets that followed. I recall very soon after this, sitting at the table one evening eating 7 slices of toast and butter thinking it was great that I could eat as much as I wanted and that my poor sister could only eat what she was given. Perhaps subconsciously I knew that eventually I would be joining my sister on a diet, so I had better enjoy my freedom to eat what I want and as much as I want now.

As predicted not long after my sister had been informed that she was going on a diet, I too was about to join her and was duly informed of this by my mother when I was around 13yrs.

This continued for both of us throughout our adolescence. Neither my sister or I were fat, perhaps the high end of average but not fat.

There were 4 of us but I was closest in age to my older sister and we shared most things together during that time. Our parents very controlling, and my mother never allowed anyone to take anything out the fridge without her knowledge or consent. If you did, all hell would break loose. Each item in the fridge was for a particular mealtime or event.

I recall on one occasion when I had my best friend to stay and my mother was busy as usual entertaining guests. We were hungry and wanted something to eat, so my friend suggested looking in the fridge. As I opened the fridge door I warned her that there would probably not be anything in there that we were allowed to eat. My friend seemed very confused and resigned herself to the fact that she would just have to stay hungry.

As I look back it would appear that my mother used food to control us to some extent. If she went out to a restaurant with my father she would often come home with a "doggy bag" for us with many of our favourite foods. Allowing us to eat these at that time but if she had placed the "doggy bag" in the fridge and we had taken the liberty of eating something from it without asking, then that would not be acceptable. She had to be in control of the food and the fridge in the house, and remains so, to this day.

The way I dealt with this was to stick with the control aspect of eating and I might have been described as a controlled eater, very conscious of the health and fitness aspect of diet. I always tried to control my weight by denying myself enough food or denying myself food that may cause my weight to increase. I didn't really stick to any particular diet other than my own restrictive one. Again subconsciously I probably did this to seek approval from my mother asking her to comment on how slim she thought I was.

At this time both my sister and I started smoking. I am not sure why but for me I would often rebel quite strongly when I felt I was being controlled and smoking was one way of dealing with this. On the other hand perhaps it was simply to help reduce the real physical hunger pangs or it may even have been to help us deal with the denial and suppression of our feelings. Obviously I was dealing with this by denying my feelings and therefore denying myself enough food and also denying myself the pleasure associated with eating the so called forbidden foods.

Eventually aged 30 something, I realised that I had developed a possible yeast intolerance but by the time I reached 40yrs of age I understood this to be a wheat intolerance combined with other multiple food intolerances. At this point I could eat literally nothing without my body reacting negatively to it in some way. Often resulting in skin rashes, constipation, headaches, irritable bowel syndrome, bloating, fatigue and just generally feeling crap.

During this time what I saw happening in the rest of my life was quite astonishing. As I became intolerant to many, many foods, I also found myself becoming extremely intolerant and critical of myself and of others. This negativity also projected into my personal relationships, my work and often while driving. Slowly I found myself withdrawing from most forms of socialising, especially if it involved food. I think I may have been subconsciously using my intolerance to food to distance and protect myself from people.

My experience had taught me that people could really hurt me. At this point I had lost the ability to trust anyone and it was much safer to withdraw from most things than risk the possibility of anyone hurting or rejecting me. I felt so sad, so out of control, so scared and so alone. In a strange sort of way I felt abandoned, but I think I had abandoned myself and really didn't understand at that point what was happening to me.

CHAPTER 1

"When we lose twenty pounds... we may be losing the twenty best pounds we have! We may be losing the pounds that contain our genius, our humanity, our love and honesty." (Woody Allen)

DIETS DON'T WORK

Diets do all sorts of things to you but what they are supposed to do. They lull you into false sense of security, they make you believe you have found the answer to all your problems and promise you all sorts of things that never really come true. So why do we all believe what they say, why do we all think that every new diet is 'the one', I am sorted now. Why? Because we are desperate, we find it hard to accept ourselves just as we are, we dislike our bodies, we are fed up not feeling happy with how we look, we don't like the shape we are, if only my legs were a bit thinner, if only I could just loose this bit around my middle, we are fed up having 2 wardrobes, one when we feel fat and one when we feel thin...the list is endless.

Diets require people to change their eating habits over a fairly long period of time and a great deal of willpower is required to stick with it. In the beginning our willpower is strong and we are usually very motivated to succeed. Our willpower is very dependent on our lifestyles, how we are feeling and what is going on in our lives on a day to day basis. When the stresses and strains begin to take their toll and we start to slip up, our willpower weakens and we succumb to the temptations of that big cream cake. People can experience dieting as deprivation, rather than behaviour change. Often the diets people choose are very restrictive and result in feelings of physical hunger and powerful cravings which can then lead to "failure". Feelings of inadequacy then creep in believing that "yet again I have failed" and a return to eating everything and anything resumes, stating that "I will start my diet again tomorrow". This can cause Yo-Yo dieting which eventually results in the pounds slowly creeping on each time a new diet starts or ends.

The message we get from the diet industry is that we are not all right as we are. The diet industry makes us believe that our worth can only be measured in terms of physical beauty, by our body size and shape. Without physical beauty we will never find true love, happiness or acceptance, unless we are physically perfect we are worthless. Research suggests that less than 5% of people who diet lose weight. Diets just don't work, people continually feel deprived when dieting and because the majority of diets are time limited, what happens when the diet ends? The person resumes their normal eating pattern for a while, slowly gains back the weight and then has to start all over again.

Sticking to a diet, depriving ourselves of many of the foods we enjoy encourages us to hate the foods we enjoy and enjoy the foods we hate. Ignoring all our internal cues that we associate with eating and pleasure can cause us to feel very deprived. Over time this feeling of deprivation can build up and lead to binge eating. When this happens many people feel overwhelmed and out of control. Feeling so out of control can be scary making us believe that we have lost control. Eventually we become completely consumed by our incessant thinking about food and eating, allowing different cravings to take hold.

What does this tell us? It tells us that by denying our individual needs we develop a separation of mind and body and begin to see food as the enemy. We ignore our internal cues, something we would never do as babies. As babies we cry when hungry, eat when we get the internal cues, and stop when full or not hungry anymore. As babies if we didn't want anymore, we would press our lips tightly together, turn our heads to the side or push our plate away. It is quite clear when a baby does not want any more to eat. As babies our cues to eat are internal and intuitive but as we develop and grow, this changes as we are trained to respond to external cues such as eating at set times and not always when we are hungry. Eventually we follow what our eyes see and want rather than what we really need. This can lead to a lack of self-control and self-discipline which is what dieting is all about.

Diets fail to address the emotional side of overeating which can lead to many people eating to help them deal with emotional problems and not because they are hungry. People often turn to food for emotional comfort because of a bad day at work or after an argument or just because they are feeling unhappy. Emotional problems cannot be solved by eating and can often result in overeating or other eating disorders. Rather than paying attention to what we're eating, and enjoying it, we detach from the experience and get lost in thoughts and feelings. We eat with our minds elsewhere and then wonder why we're still hungry, unsatisfied and looking for more when we are finished. This then becomes a vicious cycle eating when we feel bad and then feeling bad because of what we have eaten.

The main reason this eating cycle continues is because of these deeply held beliefs. In order to avoid pain and suffering we indulge ourselves in ways that we have begun to believe will satisfy us or ease our pain. What many of us don't realise is that we can change this.

Intuition is our life guide it is our inner ability of knowing or sensing without using our minds to rationalise it. Our intuition is a natural innate part of who we are but sadly over time many of us have lost our ability to get in touch with it. We ignore the subtle messages we receive, preferring to follow the rational and logical thinking projected by our minds. Getting in touch with your inner knowing and learning to trust the information you receive can be re-learned in a relatively short period of time. As you begin to use the process of Mindful Eating you will begin to reconnect with your inner voice.

TIPS

Here are a few tips to get you thinking and behaving differently around food:

♦ Stop reading diet articles and information about new diets. If you do this you will find it easier to resist the temptation to begin a new diet

♦ Begin to listen to what your body wants and forget dieting

♦ Don't panic when you start to eat all those "forbidden foods". This will all settle down in time

♦ Eating freely what you want may make you feel out of control and you may consider going back on another diet........**Don't**

- If at any time you find yourself saying "I was good today", I didn't eat that chocolate biscuit. Go right over to the biscuit tin and have that chocolate biscuit. Then you can say" Great, I'm making progress".

- Listen to your needs, stop depriving yourself, sit down and start to enjoy what you eat

ACTIVITY
Mindful eating exercise

Stop before you eat anything and just think what am I feeling? Where am I feeling this in my body?
If you are eating in response to an event, ask yourself what has just happened that has made me feel this way?
Then when you begin to eat again stop and think what am I feeling while I eat this?
When you have finished the food ask yourself how you feel and if you feel any differently to how you felt before you ate the food, do you feel better, worse, are you able to stop?

Doing this exercise and becoming more aware of yourself, what you are eating and why you are eating it in each moment will help you identify and choose foods that you want because of their nutritional content and not because of how they make you feel. It will also help you to understand how you can make a difference the next time. If you find it easier, why not write this down and then you can refer back to it and see if you notice any kind of patterns or behaviours develop over time.

CHAPTER 2

"In between stimulus and response there is a space, in that space lies our power to choose our response in our response lies our growth and our freedom." (Viktor Frankl, M.D)

<u>MINDFULNESS</u>

Have you ever found yourself sitting in front of an empty plate wondering what the food tasted like that you had just eaten or been to the cinema and bought a large tub of popcorn and reached in for another handful of popcorn only to realise that you had completely finished the tub. You had been so engrossed in the film you barely noticed what you had eaten or how much you were eating? Or have you ever been on a long journey to a friend's house, only to arrive there without being aware of what you saw along the way or even if you actually spoke to anyone on your journey? This is known as automatic pilot and I am sure many of you will relate to these situations especially when it comes to driving. Many of us often startle ourselves while driving, when we realise we have just driven 100miles and hardly remember the journey at all....quite scary really!

By living our lives in automatic pilot or in a "mindless" way we can and do miss out on so many wonderful experiences. It also impacts our health and relationships and over time can cause our emotional, physical and psychological health to break down. Eventually our bodies begin to react to this mindless stimulus in different ways. Some reactions might include stress and tension in the body, anxiety or depression. Or, we may even succumb to more addictive habits like smoking or excessive drinking. Many of us believing that this will ease our pain and help us cope more effectively, as we continue to fill our heads to bursting capacity with negative thoughts and beliefs about ourselves.

There is a way in which we can help ourselves become more centred and peaceful and that is by practicing mindfulness. Mindfulness is about staying or being in the moment and accepting whatever is happening in that moment. Many of us spend much of our time focused either on the past or on the future, and pay very little attention to what is happening in the present. This means that for much of the time we may be unaware of what we are experiencing in that moment. Mindfulness is the practise of staying in the moment, spending more time present to ourselves, and our surroundings. Not trying to change things but accepting the way that things are without criticism or judgement. Mindfulness includes both mental and physical components and emphasizes a mind-body connection. It can be a very worthwhile practice for anyone who wants to reduce stress, manage pain, or bring about a sense of awareness. Becoming more mindful is something which takes time and practice but like beginning anything new, over time the more we practice, the more we improve.

If you are prepared to make the effort and bring mindfulness to different situations and experiences that arise in your day to day life you might be surprised to notice how seldom you are really aware of what you are doing. You can become mindful in any situation it is just a matter of remembering to do it. Focusing your mind in the present rather than letting it drift away or attach to past situations or future expectations. A simple way to begin might be to make the decision to notice everything as you walk the dog every morning. This means noticing everything, whatever you are hearing, seeing, tasting, smelling, touching, or even thinking.

As you practice mindfulness you will begin to feel more relaxed in your life and you will begin to notice more things, including more painful things. This is progress and you are not doing anything wrong. The challenge here is to accept whatever is arising with love and compassion for your self, while watching the experience as it unfolds. By allowing those painful memories and feelings to be there without moving to hide them, fix them or get rid of them you will increase your chances of healing and transformation.

TIPS

Here are a few tips on how to be more mindful in your day to day lives:

- Do one thing at a time. If you are having a bath, just have a bath. If you are speaking on the phone then just talk, don't try and do other things while you are talking on the phone, having a bath or whatever.

- Do things slowly and with intention. We often rush when we do things so that we can get on to the next thing more quickly. Completely missing the experience of what we are doing. Take your time, slow down, be deliberate in your actions and focus on the task.

- Reduce your workload. Reducing your workload means that you can spend more time on the tasks you do. Giving yourself more time to do things allows you to concentrate and focus on the task in hand. Often as we do routine daily tasks or chores we find ourselves thinking of other things we should be doing or perhaps we find ourselves dwelling on or thinking about what we will do next. People often make the excuse that they are too busy that they can't possibly do less but you can. It is just a matter of prioritizing and letting go of what is not important.

♦ Manage your time. Manage your work so that you have time to complete each task. Leave plenty of time between each task. This gives you more time to spend on each item on your list and time to breathe and relax in between.

♦ Take time out and just sit in silence for a few minutes. Become aware of your thoughts. Focus on your breathing. Notice the world around you. Become comfortable with the silence and stillness.

♦ Be present. Stop worrying or thinking about what has already gone in the past and what might happen in the future. Notice your thoughts and what you keep dwelling on. Is it the past, the future or the present? Learn to recognize when you're doing this, and then practice bringing yourself back to the present. Just focus on what you're doing, right now. Enjoy the present moment.

♦ Just Listen! How often do you engage in conversation with someone and pretend to listen. We nod our heads in agreement, smile in the right places but are quite simply not there and not really listening. Our minds are on what we are going to cook for dinner tonight or how we are going to spend our week-end. Perhaps we are thinking about what we want to say next, instead of really listening to that person? Why not focus on being present, and really listen and fully enjoy being in the moment listening to the other person.

♦ Enjoy your food. How often do you really take the time to enjoy your food? So many of us eat on the run, when driving, while at work, on the phone and then wonder why we get indigestion. Take your time, sit down, eat slowly and savour each bite. Really taste your food and you may be surprised at how much better you feel.

♦ Change your attitude to routine tasks. Doing housework is another great way to practice mindfulness. Cooking and cleaning can often seem very boring. Instead of facing them with a negative attitude, put your entire mind into those tasks, concentrate, and do them slowly and completely. It could change your entire day and you get a cleaner house too.

♦ Keep practicing. It's just a matter of time until this practice becomes a regular part of your daily life.

ACTIVITY

Mindful Meditation

Sit or lie down and make yourself comfortable and make sure you will not be disturbed. Close your eyes and relax.

Begin by taking a deep breath. As you inhale deeply, draw your breath up from the base of your naval and slowly exhale gently expelling all the air in your lungs. Do this 3 or 4 more times and just be aware of your abdomen as it gently expands. Each time you inhale deeply notice as your abdomen gently contracts each time you expel the air from your lungs.

Focus all of your attention on your breath and imagine yourself slowly drifting away, far away from your daily routines and concerns. As you feel your body becoming heavier and more relaxed, notice the space and time between each breath. Let go of any thoughts, memories or emotions as they arise without any judgment or criticism. Just notice and be aware of how you feel and what is happening in each moment. Remember there is no right or wrong way to feel while you are doing this. The way you are feeling in each moment is exactly right for you. Accept and acknowledge how you are feeling in each moment and give yourself permission to experience each moment just as you are.

As you begin to feel very relaxed and fully aware of your body bring all your attention to your toes and feet. Notice how they feel, are they warm or are they cold, are you holding any tension or tightness in your toes or feet. Then.... with each out breath, feel yourself relaxing more and more, letting go of any resistance. Feel your toes and feet softly and gently relax.

Now with your next out breath bring all your attention to your legs and thighs. Notice how they feel, are they warm or are they cold, are you holding any tension or tightness in your legs or thighs. Then.... with each out breath, feel yourself relaxing more and more, letting go of any resistance. Feel your legs and thighs softly and gently relax. With each exhalation feel yourself relax into what is happening and just allow yourself to be present in each moment.

Now focus all your attention on your arms. Notice how they feel, are they warm or are they cold, do you have any discomfort in your arms, or are you holding any tension or tightness. Then.... with each out breath, feel yourself relaxing more and more, letting go of any resistance. Feel your arms softly and gently relax. With each exhalation feel yourself relax into what is happening and just allow yourself to be present in each moment.

Continue with this process until you have scanned and relaxed your whole body. Thoughts will come and go as you practice this simple technique and throughout the process you will be distracted by something. This is normal. Again just notice that you are being distracted and let the distraction go. If you find this difficult don't judge or criticize yourself just accept that this is what is happening in this moment and know that it will pass. Then continue to focus on your breathing.

Don't give up, no matter how many times you feel you are being distracted, no matter how often your mind wanders, keep at it and know that you are certainly not wasting your time. The whole point of this exercise is to practice becoming more focused. It is not something that can be rushed and does take time, patience and perseverance. Sometimes it will be easier than others. Just going through the discipline of setting aside some time and doing your best is in itself focusing on the task in hand. So remember to praise yourself and don't get too disheartened. Going through the process you are already learning how to be more mindful.

This type of practice can be done anywhere, you don't need to lie down and can last as long as you want or can manage. You may prefer to go and sit somewhere that is quiet and you are alone or you may be the type of person who can do this as you travel to work on the bus or the train. It doesn't matter as long as it suits you. Initially perhaps practice for 3 minutes per day and work up to 10-20 minutes at a time. Eventually you will begin to master this practice and will find the process of mindful eating much easier to follow. Being more mindful will have become second nature to you.

CHAPTER 3

"May we transform our unskilful states of mind and learn to eat in moderation". One of the five contemplations by

Thich Nhat Hanh (Thầy)

MINDFUL EATING

Mindful Eating is not a new concept and is about listening to what our body is telling us about our hunger and satisfaction. It is about abundance and not deprivation. Ask yourself the question. Am I really hungry? Then listen to what your body tells you. When you really get in touch with what is going on in your body and your mind it becomes much easier to know in that moment when you feel full and satisfied or when your desire to eat is more about how you are feeling in that moment. It is about understanding why, what, when, where and how we eat. It is about being compassionate and non-judgmental allowing us to look more closely at our behaviours.

Mindful eating involves paying full attention to everything you are experiencing while eating and drinking. Being aware what is happening around you and within you. What is happening in the environment you are eating in, is the TV on, are the children running around screaming or are you eating alone. Paying close attention to the food itself, how it looks, smells, tastes, is it hot or cold etc. Do you really feel hungry, where do you feel the hunger, are you getting full, is the food satisfying your hunger? Really being aware of what is happening in your body.

Recognising when we need to eat is one of the most natural ways in which our bodies communicate with us. Sadly over time we have come to ignore and manipulate these natural cues primarily caused by external factors. Such cues can range from our desire to be a certain weight, our need to conform to a certain image, our belief that we are not acceptable as we are or by using food to comfort us. Allowing this mind/body separation prevents us from really getting in touch with our inner knowing and drives us to seek information and guidance from external sources rather than trusting our own innate wisdom.

Paying attention to the mind is also necessary by observing anything that distracts attention away from the eating experience through our thoughts, without attaching to the distraction, just watching while the mind gets distracted. Observing any reactions that arise after taking a bite or a drink, like getting up to answer the phone, or making a call. Carry on eating and just notice your reactions. Notice how eating affects your feelings and moods and how your emotions like depression, sadness, fear, anxiety etc influence your eating. When all this is going on don't judge or criticize, just watch what is happening.

People eat for a variety of reasons and these reasons can often be very complex and difficult to understand. We often find that people eat when they are alone or for comfort when feeling upset while others eat to be sociable and may prefer to go out to a restaurant to eat. Some people eat at particular times throughout the day while others eat out of habit or because it serves them in some way.

As you begin to embrace mindful eating you will find that you become more mindful in general which helps promote peace of mind. You will also experience more pleasure associated with eating and start to enjoy your food more while experiencing food in new ways. As you become more intuitive you will begin to choose healthier foods, not because you think this is right but because you are correctly interpreting your body's needs for a particular food/nutrient. You will have a better understanding of hunger and become more conscious of why you eat when you are not really hungry. You will start noticing what happens in both your mind and body when you are hungry and this will begin to change the more aware you become of it. Your weight may change. Eating mindfully allows you to eat more intuitively, trusting that your body knows best. As you become more accepting of yourself and your body you may be surprised at the changes you see. Mindful eating can also help reduce binge eating in obese people (dukehealth.org, 2006)

TIPS

♦ When you eat, make sure you finish your meal satisfied. If you are unsatisfied or still feel hungry after you have eaten then you will very likely be tempted to nibble or overeat at your next meal.

♦ Make sure you have plenty of food in the house that is nutritious, tasty and that you enjoy eating. Knowing that you have plenty of what you enjoy available all the time helps prevent any thoughts of deprivation.

♦ Always eat what you want not what you have been told you should. If there are times when you don't mind what you eat then choose the healthier option e.g. eat the brown bread option instead of the white or eat the fresh fruit salad and cream instead of the chocolate cake

- Be more creative with your preparation and cooking and add nutritional value whenever you can. Use fruit and vegetables daily.

- Always check in with yourself to ensure that you are feeling hungry and not feeling, tired, upset, anxious or whatever and focus on how your stomach feels. Remember to stop eating when your stomach feels full.

- Be good to yourself, take exercise you enjoy, rest when you feel tired and really start noticing how your body communicates with you

- Go easy on your self. This is something new you are learning and it will take time to adjust and learn how to take notice of your self and how you are feeling and reacting.

ACTIVITY
Hot Chocolate for your soul

This is a fun and simple exercise for you to do. It will introduce you to the experience of how enjoyable and different mindful eating can be.

What you will need:
A cup or mug
Hot Chocolate drinking powder
Milk (Full Fat or Semi Skimmed) you choose, full fat makes it creamier
Chocolate Flake
Whipped cream

Heat up milk in saucepan and mix in 2/3 heaped teaspoons of drinking chocolate, whip up cream and put a generous dollop of cream on top and then sprinkle with some flaked chocolate.

Pick up the cup or mug and hold it with both hands.

Take a deep breathe and focus your attention completely on what you are holding in your hands.

Really feel the warmth of the hot chocolate radiating through the cup as you hold it between your hands.

Bring your face close to the cup and notice how the steam and aroma spread over your face and up your nose.

Notice the sensations inside your nose and feel the moisture on your face as the steam gently settles and begins to cool.

Notice the chocolate flake melting on the top.

Then carefully place your lip on the edge of the cup and hold it there just for a moment while resisting any temptation to take a sip.

Notice how you are feeling as you focus all your attention on the Hot Chocolate.

Do you feel happy or sad or perhaps you feel a kind of warm soft glow around you?

Just notice and be aware of how you feel and what is happening in each moment.

Remember there is no right or wrong way to feel while you are doing this.

Notice what is happening inside your mouth, is your mouth watering?

How does the cup feel against your lip?

Take a small sip and hold the warm silky liquid in your mouth again resisting any temptation to swallow.

As you hold the liquid in your mouth notice any thoughts or feelings or sensations?

How much do you really want to swallow the liquid?

Notice how long you are able to hold the liquid in your mouth without feeling the urge to swallow.

Notice the taste, the texture, the temperature, the aroma.

Notice any sensations you feel in your mouth and where you feel them.

I wonder are your eyes closed or open?

Is the taste sweet or bitter, do you find it smooth and creamy, is it still hot or has it gone cold?

Did you manage to take a sip without getting the whipped cream on your nose?

As you swallow the liquid notice the feeling as it travels down your throat and gently settles in your stomach?

Then continue to drink the rest of your Hot Chocolate in a mindful way.

When you have finished your Hot Chocolate think about the whole experience and how it felt. Did it feel different to how you would usually drink a cup of Hot Chocolate? This is just one simple exercise using a hot drink. You can try this with any drink, snack or meal you like and just notice what happens when you do this. Mindfulness can be used in any area of your life from walking the dog to brushing your teeth. It allows you to be present in each moment and over time will help you become much calmer and more relaxed in your daily life.

CHAPTER 4

"A hungry man is not a free man."

Adlai E. Stevenson quotes (American Politician. Governor of Illinois (1949-53) and Ambassador to the United Nations (1961-65) 1900-1965)

HUNGER

"Hunger is a feeling experienced when one has a desire to eat. It originates in the hypothalamus and is released through receptors in the liver." This is the definition given by Wikipedia. Does this definition really help us understand hunger? Yes, from a physiological perspective it does but what it does not include or consider is any emotional or sensory aspects so many of us experience on a regular basis associated with eating. It would seem from this definition that it is only physical hunger that pains us and gives us the desire to seek relief? Can food fill every type of hunger? Although the 5 senses are the main ways in which we experience hunger it is also worth noting there are other ways our eating patterns can occur.

Real Hunger: This is true physiological hunger your stomach is communicating with you. This is when you experience hunger pangs and your stomach feels empty and makes rumbling and gurgling noises. Extreme hunger can cause light headedness, irritability fatigue and difficulty concentrating. There are a number of other ways in which we believe we experience hunger on a regular basis. Unfortunately we wrongly interpret these signs and end up eating when we are not truly hungry. The following types of hunger are some of the ways in which we interpret a false sense of hunger.

Emotional Hunger: This is when you eat to make yourself feel better. People often comfort eat chocolates or crisps or sweets when they feel sad, anxious etc This type of hunger can often be experienced as a craving and can be a much more powerful feeling than real physical hunger. It tends to focus on just one food type and occurs more in the mouth than the stomach

Habit Hunger: This happens when we are accustomed to an eating schedule. So if we are used to eating our meals at specific times throughout the day then even when we are not hungry at those times, we will think of eating because our mind is so used to eating at those times. This is not real hunger. Often the hunger will pass if we are too busy to eat at that particular time.

Cellular Hunger: This can happen due to poor diet or a lack of nutrients but can also be expressed as a craving. This sometimes happens in pregnancy when for no particular reason a craving for a specific food happens. People often get a continual urge for a particular type of food and just can't stop craving that particular food. This can be because they are lacking a particular nutrient and continue to crave certain foods in an attempt to provide the body with the nutrient that is missing. This is a type of 'cellular hunger'. People with these nutrient deficiencies can begin to crave the wrong foods and often try and satisfy it with their favourite foods.

Mind Hunger: This is when we have thoughts about food or eating food and then struggle with whether or not we should eat the food. This is often one of the dilemmas people have who suffer with overeating or obesity problems, often chastising themselves for not being able to control the urge to eat. Especially if they consider that food, as a food they have classed as a 'Bad' food or 'Not Allowed Food'

EXPERIENCING HUNGER THROUGH THE 5 SENSES

The eyes: What you see is what you want. The well known saying of "my eyes were bigger than my belly" helps us understand how we can sometimes overeat. An example of this could be when you have just finished your meal and are full and satisfied but your friend who is eating with you orders a dessert. When you see her desert arrive, you just can't resist and you order one too. According to research people eat 24% less food when blindfolded (obesity research)

The nose: The smell of food 'is' stronger and more tempting when you are hungry. The smell of freshly baked bread or freshly brewed coffee can often make our mouths water. As you become full and satisfied the smell of food becomes less attractive and less tempting. Notice when you eat a meal that after you have eaten approximately half the plate that you no longer have the same desire to eat it as you did when you started. You may also notice that when your nose is blocked or you have a cold, you don't have much appetite.

The taste-buds: After a meal you may feel very full but somehow not satisfied. This can often be because you have eaten something salty or savoury but would still like the taste of something sweet. We usually eat what we enjoy or crave and over time we eat a lot of the same things. It is possible to retrain your taste buds to enjoy other foods.

The sense of touch: This evokes words such as feeling, texture, and sensation. Eating would be impossible without the sense of touch. Touch can be experienced in a number of ways before and during a meal and informs us of the texture and temperature of food such as crunchy, smooth, lumpy, chewy, crumbly gritty. Often when we eat foods that are crunchy (nuts) or chewy (meat) and take longer to chew, they will often make you feel full for longer because they take longer to digest.

The ears – Hearing the sound of food sizzling in a pan or someone biting into a juicy apple can cause us to salivate and desire that food. Listening to music can also affect the speed we eat at. If the music is slow and soothing we are more inclined to slow down and speed up if the music is faster.

TIPS

♦ Next time you eat a meal try closing your eyes halfway through the meal or for more fun why not eat your meal blindfold or in the dark. You might just be surprised at the difference it makes, allowing you to really get in touch with how full your stomach feels.

♦ During a meal notice how the smell of the food becomes less attractive as you become full. Smell the food before you put it in your mouth. If you are no longer tempted then you have probably had enough to eat.

- Try substituting a low fat food such as semi skimmed milk or low fat crisps for your regular ones over a 3 week period and see what happens. You might be surprised at how quickly and easily your taste preferences change.

- Always try to choose foods that take longer to chew, e.g raw foods rather than cooked

- If you find it hard to eat without listening to music, then listen to calming music such as classical or choose a restaurant that plays gentle relaxing music.

ACTIVITY
Hunger scale

The Hunger Scale Chart on the next page will help you identify how hungry you really are. Copy out this chart and over time you will then be able to work out what triggers you have and what type of hunger you are experiencing. You can also use this chart to rate your hunger on the scale throughout the day and before, during and after your meals. Notice how your hunger changes.

HUNGER SCALE

Hunger Scale	Comments
0 Starving	
1 Very Hungry stomach rumbling	
2 Hungry and need to eat	
3 A Little hungry	
4 Content not hungry or full	
5 Satisfied food in stomach	
6 Hunger is gone	
7 Feeling you have eaten too much	
8 Starting to feel uncomfortable	
9 Very Uncomfortable Need to loosen waistband	
10 Extremely uncomfortable stomach painful	

CHAPTER 5

"There ain't no such thing as wrong food"
(Sean Stewart, Perfect Circle, 2004)

THE FOOD AND MOOD CONNECTION

What we eat can also affect how we feel both physically and emotionally. Understanding the connection between food and mood can help us alter our mood by changing our diet and making different food choices. Different foods contain different amounts of an amino acid called tryptophan. Tryptophan is converted by the body to serotonin which is an important brain chemical that regulates impulse control and appetite, elevates mood and self-esteem, increases feelings of optimism and induces calm feelings and sleep. If serotonin levels become consistently low, we can begin to feel quite low, depressed and tired without really knowing or understanding why this is happening.

While refined products such as white flour, biscuits, pastries, and sugar can elevate serotonin levels quickly, making you feel good, this only lasts for a short period. The reason this happens is because refined carbohydrates cause the brain to produce too much serotonin too quickly causing the brain to shut off producing any more serotonin in order to help restore balance. This results in our bodies becoming less able to use the serotonin we have and unable to function optimally without again craving that sugar boost which eventually results in a cycle leading to low mood caused by chronic low serotonin levels.

Good mood protein such as chicken, fish, meat, eggs, dairy, beans, nuts seeds and avocado can improve mood as they contain high amounts of tryptophan. Good mood carbohydrates are concentrated in pasta (preferable corn), brown rice, oats and fruit. To help absorption of tryptophan into the brain we need to eat slow releasing carbohydrates. Carbohydrate cravings have been explained as a subconscious drive to increase serotonin levels. The oats are particularly important because they have a low Glycaemic Index. Eating foods with a low GI, which release their energy slowly and keep you feeling good for longer, can help to avoid the roller coaster ride of energy and moods associated with large fluctuations in blood glucose levels. The natural sugars in the fruit have a gentler effect on the blood sugar levels than added, refined sugar.

Good mood fats are also essential for the body to be able to use serotonin effectively and are contained in oil rich fish, nuts and seeds. The brain contains over 60% fat. Avoiding all types of fat - in a low fat diet for example - can lead to anxiety and depression and other mental health problems. Polyunsaturated 'omega 3' fats are particularly important and these are particularly high in the oily rich fish and also present in pumpkin seeds and walnuts. You need to keep a balance between the omega 3 fats and the other essential 'omega 6' fats which, in a well balanced meal are found in the nuts and seeds. Vitamins and minerals are also essential for emotional and mental health. For example the conversion of the tryptophan to serotonin is helped by various 'co-factor' nutrients such as Vitamin C, Folic acid, Vitamin B6, Zinc, Biotin and Selenium. There are a number of foods that can give rise to poor mood particularly in large amounts and include:

Artificial additives can cause a range of food sensitivity reactions in certain people

Added sugar can cause a sudden blood sugar rise followed by a dip in mood and energy an hour or so later. Sugar sensitivity can produce symptoms of confusion, poor concentration, anxiety, irritability, aggression, fatigue and depression.

Stimulants such as chocolate or caffeine which can be associated with feelings of anxiety or panic attacks in vulnerable people

Wheat or dairy foods are the two most common culprit foods associated with food sensitivities and have been associated with depression and fatigue

Foods that are low in additives, refined sugar or added sugar, low in stimulants such as coffee, chocolate etc and are hypoallergenic are much more likely to make us feel good. A well balanced meal that will help to promote feelings of well being over a long period of time is likely to contain essential fats, particularly omega 3 food sources, be high in complex carbohydrates (or low Glycaemic Index foods), high in fruit and vegetables for vitamins and minerals and contain some protein.

When we feel bad we eat comfort foods like too many saturated fats such as chocolate, chips etc or simple carbohydrates like biscuits and sweet treats which gives us a very short-term high. The more we eat of those foods the shorter the high lasts which means we continually eat more to feel good but eventually this just makes us feel worse but still wanting more and so the cycle continues. The following true story is in some respects a perfect example of how too much of certain foods can affect our moods and how this becomes a vicious cycle.

REBECCAS STORY

"I am a 56 year old woman and have struggled on and off with diets and comfort eating for most of my life. I have come to understand that I have a wrongful association with food. Thinking back to my childhood, my earliest memory of food problems started when I was around 8 or 9 years of age. In fact one earlier memory is of being wrongfully punished, being smacked and put to bed for eating a whole packet of Jammy dodgers. My sister had eaten them. (I hated jammy dodgers then, and still do).

Sweets were allowed as a special treat, especially on a Friday night, when dad came home from the pub. I also bought myself a Mars bar with the money I got from Mum on a Saturday, when I helped her clean out the Doctors surgery where she worked. Maybe this was the start of comfort eating, as chocolate is now an addiction for me. When I was younger I also suffered from very severe migraine headaches, which seemed to get worse when I felt nervous, especially at test times in school.

All through my life food has been a source of comfort to me. When I am excited and happy about things I eat chocolate or cakes. When I am feeling down I eat chocolate or cakes.

My addiction to sweet foods seems particularly influenced by my moods. Often when I awake in the morning my first thought is for chocolate, and also when I finish a meal, I feel I need something sweet to eat.

There have been times when I have been successful at dieting and have felt good about my weight and appearance, but these feelings never seem to last long. When I eat sweet foods I feel really content and satisfied, but I never seem to be able to stop at one sweet. Sometimes I continue eating sweet food until I feel bloated and sleepy. These are the times when I get a bit down with myself, and find myself caught up in a cycle of elation and sedation.

During my career with the Police service I became very disillusioned and again found that what I was eating was very much influenced by how I was feeling. At this time I ate mostly stodgy sweet food, and very little vegetables and fruit. White bread was a major component of my diet. Eating at very strange times didn't help, especially when working nightshift.

The emotions I go through with food are difficult to explain. I know when I eat chocolate or food that I class as wrong food, that it is not good for me in the long term. Yet I seemed to feel better after stuffing my face with sugary foods. The main effects I usually experience are an initial burst of energy (feeling elated), followed by tiredness, which has at times caused me to fall asleep during the day.

On other occasions when I have been on a health kick, and felt good about my appearance, despite knowing I was overweight (I am still overweight), I had energy and could walk for long periods. My joints didn't ache, and I slept better. There was no loss of energy in the afternoons. The only problem was, although I enjoyed the healthy food, I still didn't feel satisfied.

I have asked myself if the constant need for satisfaction in eating the wrong food could be linked to my emotions and deep rooted fears (known or unknown to me). I think they are, but as yet I have not found the solution to eradicate this feeling.

Today, again I am beginning another diet and I am 3 days into eating more healthily. I have drastically cut out the intake of bread, white or brown. I am eating raw vegetables with a healthy option dip in place of chocolate or cakes, and as a snack. I seem to benefit by eating small amounts more often. I find when I have not been able to eat at regular times or a meal time has been delayed, this is when I binge, or find it difficult to stop eating once I start. I have been exercising regularly for over 6 months. I feel fitter but once again when my weigh-in time comes and it is not good news, the thought to comfort myself with chocolate always comes to mind. I often wonder!!!! Is it my digestive system that rules my cravings or is it all in my mind? I know some foods are very mind and mood altering.

I often wonder should I look to my early childhood to find the answers to my failings with food or do I bite the bullet and deal with the ups and downs of life without the need for chocolate or other sweet foods? I like eating. It would be impossible for me to survive without food. The feelings I have when eating the wrong foods are a mixture of emotions ranging from "Aaaah" to "Oh Sod it". I KNOW WHAT FOODS ARE WRONG, BUT.........."

What are your thoughts and feelings about this story? Do you really think there are "Wrong Foods" or that we can have a "Wrongful Association" with food? Rebecca's story quite clearly highlights the "Food and Mood" cycle that so many of us get caught up in trying to find a way to make ourselves feel better.

TIPS

♦ If you find yourself feeling anxious, sad, moody or really don't know how you feel. Don't do what you have always done and just reach out and eat the first thing that comes to hand. Take some time just to work out what is happening, what you are feeling, why you are feeling it and what has caused it. Only by understanding and being able to alter habits and patterns will you begin to change your relationship with food.

♦ It's ok to snack on any food you want but bear in mind that high glycaemic foods will boost your mood and make you feel satisfied for longer e.g. dried fruit and seed bars. What ever you do don't deprive yourself of what you want as this will only make you crave it more.

♦ Remember enjoy what you eat and don't deny your self anything. This is just the beginning and over time you will be amazed and how mindful you become.

♦ If your hunger isn't satisfied after eating what you grab and you continue to want more and more, then the chances are it probably isn't real hunger.

♦ Just be aware it may often be the very foods that you crave that are affecting your mood and how you feel.

ACTIVITY

The Cloud Technique

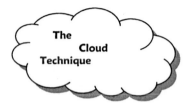

The cloud technique is a technique which allows you to change your state or emotions on your own just about anywhere. It takes less than 30 seconds and anyone can use this technique. Often we think we are our emotions/feelings and that we have no choice about them but we can in fact change how we feel. The Cloud technique allows us to do this very quickly and simply. (The Cloud Technique © 2004 Kevin Creedon)

- Imagine a situation where you felt/feel particularly uncomfortable (scared, anxious negative etc)
- Imagine the feelings as a cloud around you
- Describe the colour, size and motion of the cloud
- Then step out of it and walk away from it and look back at it. (it will disappear quickly with no human there to create the emotion)
- Given what you want in the big picture, ask yourself is that emotion serving you well? The answer will most likely be "No"

- Even though the cloud is beginning to disappear, blow it out like a candle.

- In another location imagine a different scenario with a different emotion (confident, happy, positive etc) that will serve you better.
- Then step into this cloud and turn on the positive feelings and emotions. Think back to the previous scenario with these positive feelings round you and feel the difference.

Use this technique whenever you are feeling particularly uncomfortable, unsure or un-resourceful and trust yourself. Respect that in some cases it may not be so easy but whatever is happening is right for you at the time.

CHAPTER 6

"All that we are is the result of what we have thought. The mind is everything. What we think we become." (Buddha)

FEELINGS AND EMOTIONS

The nature of our thoughts, feelings and intentions are reflected in our lives, our bodies and our world. Relationships are a large part of our lives and without them life might actually seem pretty pointless. Feeling the connection with another person and having them understand and support you in difficult times, or sharing a coffee and a chat are just a few of the things that make life worthwhile.

What we might not be so conscious of is that how we relate to food is often reflected in how we relate to other people or even to ourselves. Think for a moment about the relationships you have in your life right now and what they are saying about you and your relationship with food or even the relationship you have with yourself. Are you someone who is a Yo-Yo dieter, always worried about what you are eating, eating certain foods and then feeling guilty after you have eaten them. This type of relationship with food might suggest that you have little or no self worth, always worried about what people think. Believing what they think about you is important. Similarly in your relationships with your friends you may find that you always likes to please everyone all of the time and find it hard to say no, feeling guilty when you do. As long as everyone else is all right it doesn't really matter about you, you never really speak your truth or express how you are really feeling. Your relationships may then feel rather empty, meaningless and superficial.

Or are you someone who likes to be in control all the time, eats by the clock, only eats particular foods on particular days and is very choosy and fussy about what foods you eat as they don't always agree with you. Do you often come out in a rash, feel bloated, get headaches or feel very lethargic after eating certain foods etc. Again looking at your relationships with your friends you might find you hold yourself back from them, you might find it hard to trust some of them, don't really say what you feel and unconsciously choose people that may hurt you or push you around.

When you become more mindful of your relationship with food and begin to understand that you can have a healthy relationship with food. You might be surprised at how your relationships with people also begin to change and your relationship with yourself.

Many people eat because of how they are feeling. Most people give up on their diets or give in to certain foods because of emotional hunger. Feelings of emotional hunger can and do appear when you are feeling needy and perhaps seeking comfort or love and not receiving it. Emotional hunger is real and affects all of us at some time in our lives. If you address the underlying cause (the emotion/feeling) rather than the symptom (which is emotional eating) then eating will become something that is natural rather than something we feel unable to control and guilty about.

Each time an event occurs in our lives we usually react to that event and particular feelings are then generated. Feelings can seem very complex and at times may confuse us causing us to act without any sense of awareness. Although some may say we cannot control our feelings, what we can do is change the thought which often precipitates the feeling. We can choose how we want to react to something but changing the hard wiring in our brains can take time, understanding and awareness. Using meditation will help you through this process. It will allow you to get in touch with your feelings and identify what emotions and feelings you repeatedly experience before, during and after you eat.

Do you feel, bored stressed, angry, depressed, upset when you want to eat? Perhaps you feel guilty believing that you shouldn't really be eating, or disappointment that you have given in to these urges yet again. Or perhaps you are driven crazy by the continual mind chatter in your head filled with criticism and judgments about what you should and shouldn't be eating and whether this is a "good" or "bad" food. How do you deal with these thoughts and feelings?

THOUGHTS AND BELIEFS

How we feel is often connected to what we believe and this is particularly true in relation to what we believe and feel about ourselves. 90% of what you think, say and do is based on your subconscious beliefs (the stuff you are often not aware of) 80% of the beliefs you are operating on today were formed before the age of eight. For example some of us may have gone through life believing that we are stupid, possibly because of what our parents or teachers continually communicated to us as a child. The more we hear this the more we begin to believe this and when we believe something this can evoke strong feelings or emotions in us. Believing we are stupid may make us feel anxious in highly pressurized situations such as attending an interview.

How can we change this? First you have to recognize that something is causing you pain and then commit to letting this go. Again this is something that can take time, so be patient and kind with your self. Think about the way in which this pain might be serving you, how is it benefiting you or how is it holding you back? For example you may have started binge eating because someone told you, you would never amount to anything. Your response to that was to feel hurt by this persons words, fear that they might just be right and anger that they could be so cruel but you said nothing because you looked up to the person who said this to you, you believed them and thought they must be right. So when ever you remember this event and the pain that this caused, rather than deal with how you feel because it is too painful for you, or you don't know how to deal with it, you eat something because that seems to temporarily relieve the pain. Over the years as you continued to do this the weight piled on and you felt like a failure.

Once you become aware of your behaviour and recognize what has caused this and are committed to changing it or letting it go, you can then see the benefits this change will bring about. In time you will come to realize that you have a choice, to dwell on these feelings, continue to attach to the experience or stop reliving the hurt and move on. Focus on the present, acknowledge the feelings when they come back, be kind to your self but bring yourself back to the present moment and continue to do this. Eventually you will begin to feel more peaceful and rather than eating to deal with the feelings you will now be able to allow yourself to be present, allow the feelings to be there and then let them go.

The following story helps us to understand how Emma used food to provide a source of comfort to herself throughout her life to help ease her pain. During her childhood her mother provided food as a comforter to Emma when she had hurt herself physically, rather than expressing and providing physical and emotional comfort to her. To some extent Emma has continued to do this by using food to create bonds and strengthen relationships. Perhaps in some ways she has used food to allow a more intimate connection with people and has also found ways of using certain foods which have helped her cope when feeling low.

EMMAS STORY

"When I think about my relationship with food, the first thing I think about is comfort. Food provides me with comfort when I am feeling sad, bored, tired, angry or stressed. I have been able, through talking to sensitive people, friends, counsellors etc to see where the comforts of food came from, and whilst this is a useful insight, it does not necessarily change my behaviour. I am aware that this needs to come from within, and I am not there yet.

My mother was the first person to feed me, and whilst I don't want to blame her, I can see that some of my behaviour arises from the way she deals with food in our family. I know I was loved by my mother, and I think I see the comfort I receive from food as a connection with that love I received from her.

She lived through the war, rationing and hardship, and waste was seen as bad in our family. If food was put on my plate, it was to be eaten, whether the portion was an appropriate size or not. My mother also saw feeding her family as a way of showing them how much she loved them. It is not too great a step from this to see that eating the food showed her in return that I loved her too. As I grew up, if I ever left anything on my plate, my mother would question me as to what was wrong with it, usually with a hurt look on her face. I therefore needed to eat everything to show her I appreciated her and to avoid hurting her.

My mother prided herself on being a good cook, particularly at baking, and her idea of a treat was, and still is, always to bake a cake. Cakes were always a part of any celebration, from the traditional Christmas and birthdays to smaller events like bank holidays, my visiting home for the weekend as a student or bringing friends round. Large slices were expected to be eaten, and the remainder taken home in a tin. I remember these occasions with pleasure, but also tinged with irritation as my mother always looked for congratulations on the standard of her baking, and she seemed to take it as a personal slight if a second slice was refused.

On reflection, I carry out similar behaviour today. I enjoy cooking, and get a lot of pleasure from taking a cake in to work to share with colleagues. I bask in the praise of my skills, and when my children visit, I show my pleasure by cooking their favourite dishes. I feel as if this is using food to show how much I care for people, as effort has gone into its preparation. I can and do show affection in other ways too, but food is usually the most important factor.

My mother reinforced the idea of comfort eating by using food as a panacea for all ills. If my children fell over and grazed their knees, I gave them a cuddle to dry their tears, my mother always gave a biscuit, cake or sweets. If I feel hurt now, physically or emotionally, I crave something sweet, the equivalent of a cuddle.

Anger was something I was not allowed to show as a child, and the few occasions I remember losing my temper or having a tantrum still seem very vivid in my memory. They were major events and full of negative messages from my mother. It was made very clear to me that showing anger hurt her, and once the event was all over, it was "made better" with some sort of sweet treat. If I feel angry now, I often eat food very fast, hardly noticing what it is.

Sadness and the pain of depression have been factors in my life and I have often used food to help me deal with it. I use food, particularly high carbohydrate products as a way of shutting off whatever the feelings are. If I eat a large amount of high carbohydrate food like bread, biscuits or cake, the natural result is a feeling of lethargy and drowsiness, and often a long sleep. Whilst I am asleep, I feel no pain, so I suppose I am using food as a sedative.

Reading what I have written so far sounds rather negative, but I have very positive feelings towards food too. After all, meals can be sociable, form the basis of a party atmosphere and healthy food makes you feel good. I have spent many years on the dieting/bingeing roller coaster and have found that the times in my life when I have been happiest are when I have been eating moderate amounts of a variety of different foods. Different people have an effect on my eating too. When I am with someone who respects me, cares about me and does not judge me, I find that my eating habits become more like someone who does not have an eating problem. That is, stopping when I am full, and not eating unless I am hungry. That sounds pretty simple, doesn't it?

It is probably worth mentioning here about the various attempts I have made to deal with my problems with food, or its effects on my weight. I have been overweight since about the age of 10, which coincided with the development of severe psoriasis. Both my skin and my weight have been very much a measure of my emotional health over the years. When I have been at my happiest, I have been slimmer and at my most depressed, have been heavier and my psoriasis extensive and inflamed. In fact I can pinpoint the real beginning of my over-eating and consequent dieting.

I was 13 years old, very conscious of my changing body, finding being in the top stream of the grammar school quite taxing and was covered with psoriasis from head to toe. It was severe enough for the dermatologist to admit me to hospital as an emergency from the out patient clinic and I was in hospital for 6 weeks, having unpleasant ointments applied, and having to wear a special "bandage suit" to keep the grey paste off my clothes. During this time, all my friends and relations felt very sorry for me, and on visits, brought chocolates and other edible treats. I had no exercise for 6 weeks, and took comfort from eating. Consequently, by the time I was discharged, I was a size larger, and decided to start my first diet.

So the start of over 40 years of diets now begins. I have tried the grapefruit diet, Beverley Hills diet, F-Plan diet, cabbage soup diet, fasting, Cambridge diet, milkshakes, chocolate bars etc. I have been a member of Weightwatchers, Slimming World, Rosemary Conley and various other slimming groups. I have tried acupuncture, hypnosis, self help books and reflexology. I have spent probably many thousands of pounds, and am still obese.

I find that dieting brings out the manipulative side of my personality, and I usually end up disliking myself more than usual. A common pattern when going to a slimming group is to be very enthusiastic for a few weeks, feel good about my efforts then hit some sort of hurdle. This could be a night out where it is difficult to avoid "difficult" food and drink, a stressful time at work or home, an emotional or physical upset. I take this as a reason to "cheat" and then feel bad again. The pattern then tends to be that I continue with the slimming group, but don't tell the truth to the leader. I eat very little for the 3 days before I am weighed, then overeat for the next few days. I can remember many evenings at a slimming club where I have spent the majority of my time planning what I would eat on the way home.

When I decide I am going to lose weight, I usually plan when the diet is going to start, usually a Monday morning. I make sure I have lots of healthy food in the house, and plan what I am going to eat. However, I usually manage to find an excuse to eat lots during the weekend, either to "eat up" the fattening foods or to have a "last binge." This of course sets my mind into a feeling of being deprived, so I know that I am setting myself up to fail. When I am eating well and exercising regularly, I feel physically and emotionally much better, but the pattern usually repeats itself and I, like many others I know, go back to my old ways and gain the weight I have lost, plus more. Writing this out and seeing it in print makes me realise how important this issue has been for almost the whole of my life, quite a thought."

For many of us who use food as a coping mechanism and consciously control our weight by manipulating what we eat, all have very similar stories to tell. Understanding what is going on can be difficult but is often the first step to realizing just what you have been trying to do over a long period of time.

TIPS

- Write down 7 things you really like about yourself, the first 7 that come into your head.
- Write down things that you do well and also the things that you do that are not just for your own benefit.
- Write down 7 things you like about your body.
- Describe what you like when you look in the mirror.
- Write down the personal qualities you are proud of and look at them every day. When you have done this think about how easy it was, were some things easier to write down than others? If you found it hard set an intention to carry out this activity once a week until you find it easier.
- Write down how you felt as you were doing this and then reflect on why this might have been.
- Writing out affirmations can also improve how you feel about yourself.

ACTIVITY
Emotional Freedom Technique

Emotional Freedom Technique (EFT) is for anyone who wants to improve both their emotional and physical health and well-being by removing negative emotions and feelings. It was developed in America by Gary Craig in the early

1990s, from psychologist Dr Roger Callahan's 'Thought Field Therapy' and is now widely used throughout the world.

The easiest way to explain EFT is to describe it as 'Acupuncture without needles'. It involves tapping on various acupuncture points, while concentrating on a particular problem. You can overcome your fears, phobias and negative emotions using this simple technique and is very effective and often brings relief within minutes. The technique is simple and easy to learn and can be taught to anyone to use themselves on a regular basis. It can be used regularly for personal development, problem solving and stress relief. Stress, anxiety, fears, phobias, eating disorders, addictions and many more issues can be successfully treated using this technique.

EFT is not about denying, repressing or disassociating from your feelings. It will not suppress or mask symptoms or illnesses that may need medical attention. Each session typically ends with a positive result and most importantly, a neutral emotional response when thought is given to the particular issue/problem/emotion/feeling.

EFT is a process which uses a number of steps. The following process is the shortened version of the EFT procedure which can be learned and applied immediately.

4 STEP PROCESS

1) First you need to identify the issue/feeling/emotion/problem and give it an "Intensity" value, on a scale of 0 to 10 where 0 is no intensity and 10 is very strong intensity

2) Then you create a short statement or Set-up Phrase which describes the feeling/issue/emotion etc such as "Even though I have an extremely painful headache, I deeply and completely love and accept myself" As you focus on your headache you also tap on the "Karate Chop" point on the side of the hand. You repeat the statement while tapping the point 3 times.

3) You then adapt the original set-up statement using one or two key words only and make this shorter, a "reminder phrase" such as "this headache" and "extremely painful". Using 2 or more fingers repeat this phrase as you tap through the whole sequence of tapping points shown below.

4) After you have completed one or two rounds of the tapping sequence, check where your intensity level is. It may have completely gone or it may have reduced to a 3 or 4. If the level has lowered continue tapping until it has reduced to a zero.

The following are a few other "Set Up" statements you may want to use or add to, just to help you get started and used to the whole process. The EFT tapping points diagram with a description and location for each point will also help you as you go through the tapping sequence.

Examples "Set Up" Statements

1. "Even though I feel really sad and upset, I deeply and completely love and accept myself"
   Shortened version "really sad" "really upset" "feel so sad"

2. "Even though I feel really guilty and angry that I ate chips at lunchtime, I deeply and completely love and accept myself"

Shortened version "really guilty" "really angry" "chips" "lunchtime"

3. "Even though I hate myself for craving and eating chocolate every time I feel sad or low, I deeply and completely love and accept myself"

Shortened version "hate myself" "sad or low" "craving" "chocolate"

For example if using statement 3, begin by tapping using 2 or more fingers and tapping at least 7 times on each point beginning with:

Top of Head point and say "hate my self"

Tapping at Eyebrow point say "sad"

Then continue tapping at Side of Eye point say "craving"

Under Eye Point say "chocolate"

Under Nose point say "low"

Chin point say "chocolate"

Collar Bone points say "hate myself"

Under Arm point say "craving"

Then repeat the whole sequence again. One complete take a deep breath in and then assess the intensity of the feeling/emotion/issue etc giving it a score. If the intensity score is not zero then continue until it reaches zero. You will be amazed at how fast and simple it is and how different you feel.

What this will do is allow you to remove any negative thoughts, feelings or beliefs you have about yourself and the relationship you have with food. Mindful eating does not ask that you have will power, mindful eating does not ask that you deprive your self of any foods and mindful eating does not ask that you deny your thoughts, feelings or beliefs. What EFT can help you with is in allowing you to get in touch with the negative thoughts, feelings and beliefs and then let them go, using a very simple technique. EFT is not about denying yourself anything but by using this technique you will eliminate the negative thoughts, feelings and beliefs that you have come to associate with particular foods or eating and by doing this you will then feel quite differently about your relationship with food.

For example if you have always eaten chocolate every time you felt down or sad because this makes you feel better for a little while, the chances are that you may then believe that you cannot resist chocolate or that you always crave chocolate when you feel down. If you use EFT to eliminate the low or sad feelings then you will have no desire or craving for chocolate. You can eat chocolate whenever you want and in any quantity but by eliminating the core issue associated with eating the chocolate (your need to feel better) you have eliminated this thought, feeling and belief and will no longer have this craving or weakness. Your desire for chocolate will then become a healthy desire. Not a desire based on an underlying feeling and the way you eat chocolate and in what quantity will then probably change with no feelings of denial or deprivation.

EFT Tapping Points

Use the Tapping Point Chart on the next page to help you locate the different tapping points.

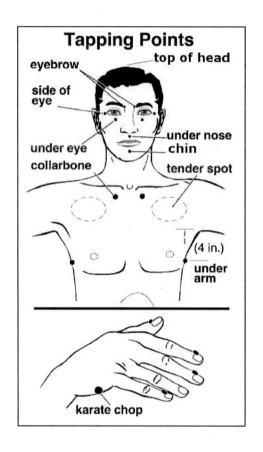

Note: Although EFT is particularly effective in treating many different conditions the technique should not be seen as a substitute for appropriate medical care. EFT should always be used in conjunction with medical consultation for such conditions. Although this is a very simple technique to follow once familiar with it, you may find it easier to refer to a more detailed explanation which can be found in many of the books written about it. Please refer to the list at the end of this book for recommended reading and websites.

CHAPTER 7

The breeze at dawn has secrets to tell you.
Don't go back to sleep. You must ask for what you really want.
Don't go back to sleep. People are going back and forth across the
door sill where the two worlds touch. The door is round and open.
Don't go back to sleep. (Rumi)

EATING TRIGGERS

Many of us often don't ever stop to consider the reasons why we eat the way we do. Overeating or binging as some might consider it, have become a way of life for so many of us. Much of this can be attributed to the various ways in which we choose to live our lives. Some of us are over worked, while others are feeling stressed and frustrated. None of us really take the time to think about why or what we are eating. We stand aimlessly in front of an open fridge door wondering why on earth we are there, our minds probably already half way down the garden path on to our next task of the day. Rushing from one thing to the next, without even giving ourselves the time to take breath let alone sit down and have a mindful cup of tea. Let's have a look at the some of the many eating triggers we can encounter on a daily basis.

Think about when the phone rings just as you are about to sit down and have dinner. You answer the phone with one hand while munching on a chicken leg with the other hand. How much attention are you putting on either of those actions? Very little, so you don't really enjoy chatting to the person on the phone because you are hungry and want to eat your dinner sitting down. You can't even enjoy what you are eating because your focus is not on the food but who you are talking to. So everyone looses out, you don't honour yourself or the food you are eating, you don't listen properly to the person on the phone and miss what they are saying and you don't enjoy the food you are eating as you are barely aware you are eating it. That is just one example of how mindless we can all be on a day to day basis.

Social Triggers: This often happens when people are encouraged or pressurized by friends, peers or those around them to eat. In an attempt to fit in or mask our feelings of inadequacy in social situations we often give in to the pressures. Christmas time, weddings, funerals etc are all social events where we are often expected to eat and/or drink.

Situational/Environmental Triggers: This is almost unavoidable and is about the surroundings or environments we eat in. Restaurants we eat in smell good, sound good (great music) and look good (displays of food and inviting table settings) so most of our senses are being stimulated when we walk into a restaurant and it's very hard to resist. Other environmental triggers might be always eating popcorn when at the cinema, always eating something when watching TV, reading a book or eating by the clock.

Physiological Triggers: This is very easy to interpret if the time is taken just to listen to what our bodies are communicating to us. A stomach rumbling and feeling very empty are sure signs of real hunger. If you are not used to listening to your body's real cues of hunger then this can take time and discipline to become familiar with. Other physiological cues might be weakness, light headedness or lack of energy.

Emotional Triggers: There are many emotional triggers to eating and overeating in many cases. The top 8 emotional eating triggers are stress, anxiety, sadness, depression, loneliness, PMS, anger and boredom. People often find some form of comfort or release by eating when experiencing emotional upset in their lives. Negative thoughts about our selves or low self-esteem can also lead to overeating or "binge eating"

Thinking Triggers: This happens when we continually want to justify to ourselves that it is okay to eat and to eat particular things. When we think about food we are often driven to go and eat that particular food, sometimes even if we have to drive some way to buy it. We attach to the mindless chatter that is going on in our heads, telling us how "bad" we are when we fail at out latest diet attempt, or that we are not perfect just as we are, that "only if" we could just change this or that then we would be a much better person or that we would feel okay about ourselves. Thinking triggers also include the "should's and shouldn'ts" I should really eat something more healthy, I should go on another diet, I shouldn't really eat this bar of chocolate, I shouldn't really have eaten that pudding. This mindless negative chatter can also slowly eat away at our self-worth and self confidence.

If we begin to examine our own eating motives, many of us may be surprised to find we have triggers from all 5 areas and that eating can become a problem when food is not used to satiate physical hunger. If you notice that food is becoming more central to your thinking and daily living, you begin putting more effort into maintaining your weight rather than maintaining your relationships with your family and friends. You find you berate yourself after eating anything. You use food to temporarily make yourself feel better. Your body image is becoming distorted and you regularly refuse food in an attempt to control your weight and body image then you may have to question whether or not eating is becoming a problem to you.

The following food diary has been included here which is very detailed and informative and allows us some insight into Christine's daily eating patterns, her food choices, her triggers and a little insight into her relationship with food. Providing this real life example may help many of you as you contemplate the reasons behind your own relationship with food and help you to complete your own Daily Eating Journal. You will find an example of this at the back of the book. If you copy the example out, you can then use it to help you monitor how you eat at the moment and then as you begin mindful eating look at how your habits begin to change. It is useful to do this prior to beginning to eat in a more mindful way as then you have some record of what changes and progress you are making.

CHRITINES FOOD DIARY

Background

Christine, age 57, married for 31 years, children aged 28 and 25. I am presently more than 2 ½ stones heavier than when married. I have only once subscribed to a formal 'slimming club' for a few months, with the usual results of some initial apparent success, but no lasting change to weight, though some lasting changes to eating patterns and attitudes. I am trying at present to eat sensibly without any sense of deprivation or punishment.

Sunday 4 October 2009

Need to be at E's house by 8 a.m. to travel to a Reiki workshop for the day. Didn't fancy breakfast at that time so put some grapes in a pot. Opened the fridge to find something for lunch - options were quiche lorraine, cold ham, cottage cheese and salad stuff. Felt uninterested in the quiche - somehow it would be too _tasty_ so packed cottage cheese, salad, cous-cous and prepared celery, nut, fruit, mayo combination and a fruit yoghourt. Even remembered the fork and spoon!

When we stopped for fuel there was an opportunity to pick up chocolate or crisps and I asked E if she wanted anything to nibble. She said no and I didn't feel the need or urge to buy anything. The grapes kept me going until lunchtime and enjoyed my salad and yoghourt which were completely satisfying. When we left at 5pm neither of us needed to go to get a snack. On the way home I learned that macaroni cheese was waiting for me at home. I wondered whether to stop for chips to have with it, but drove past the chippie without even realising it. There's a chocolate chip muffin in the kitchen but I felt no inclination to have it for supper later.

Monday 5 October

I enjoyed a lovely walk in cold sunshine with dog at 7.30. I had Jordan's muesli for breakfast with fresh raspberries and semi-skimmed milk. I always add rolled oats to the muesli to take away some of the sweetness and increase the oat to wheat ratio. Also a sprinkle of cinnamon to ward off diabetes! My daughter made me a lovely salad lunch and offered me chocolate as dessert which I had no notion for. We then went to a friend's funeral and to the 'tea' after. I visited the buffet table twice for savouries - vol-au-vents, wraps and really enjoyed the flavours and textures. With my cup of tea I HAD to have a tiny scone with jam and a small piece of chocolate ginger slice. Before we left I took another piece - it was so good. There's something about this maybe being the 'last opportunity' when it comes to sweet treats - fear of there not being another chance; when it's taken away maybe it won't ever be offered again, so I pig out on it. That was around 5.30 and I have no need to eat anything else before bed.

Tuesday 6 October

I will be working a long day at the shop, so muesli, oats and strawberries for breakfast. I prepared a box with salad and cottage cheese to take with me and a kiwi fruit and a yoghourt. Very busy morning - bought a mug of lentil soup for comfort and speed, no time to stop. Eventually ate salad around 3 p.m. - didn't have fruit or yoghourt but didn't buy any sweets or cake or chocolate either! At home put pizza in oven while changing for a quick get-out to theatre. Only managed a couple of slices of cheese pizza before lift arrived. Needed something when I got home - didn't fancy bread, or the choc chip muffin which is STILL sitting there - so had nice mushy Weetabix!

Wednesday 7 October

Had a lovely walk with Jinty at 7 a.m. Sunrise and the waning moon still bright. Only a small cereal bowl available for breakfast - the rest in the dishwasher! So I just had a little muesli and oats. Worked in the shop from 9 - 2 so had a banana around 12. No desire for anything else. No time for lunch at home as had a hair appointment after walking the dog. Had a cup of tea and a tiny cube of tablet there - very sweet, but it didn't drive me to go and buy more. Home and veg stir fry for tea. Ken suggested chocolate pudding for dessert and I enjoyed a modest portion (with a little cream) but didn't feel the need to pig out on seconds and didn't need or want anything else before bed.

Thursday 8 October

Usual breakfast, but no work this morning so around 10.30 allowed myself a coffee and ate the lonely muffin. No greed, no voraciousness (voracity?) it was just something to have with a cup of coffee. Working at 1pm. It was a busy afternoon in the shop and neither of us home before 6 so tea was a bit later. Breaded fish baked in the oven with boiled potatoes, carrots and steamed fresh broccoli and cauliflower. We had David's home made lentil soup to start and HAD to finish the chocolate pudding for dessert! No drinks or nibbles through the evening, didn't even think about them.

Friday 9 October

Opened fridge to put milk away and found a few tinned apricots left, so put them together with rolled oats, pumpkin, sesame, flax and sunflower seeds, almonds, Brazil nuts, pecans, greek yoghourt and cinnamon for a change for breakfast. (On the scales this morning I found the muffin and chocolate pudding!). Got to work not having had any lunch so had a cup of yellow split pea soup and an egg mayo roll. The trifles, puddings and sweeties in the shop held no attraction. Had tea with Amy in The Park Hotel - pan fried garlic mushrooms (very oily) and vegetable cheesy pasta.

Didn't eat it all. Had a few spoons of David's vanilla ice cream. After dinner my tummy grumbled a lot and there was a massive liquid clear out. (Gin and tonic before dinner!)

Saturday 10 October

Muesli breakfast and cup of tea then off to work. Was offered a bacon roll and ketchup at 10.30 and it appealed to me so I accepted! Nothing else to eat until 7 p.m. - cheese/veg bake with carrots and potatoes and apple crumble with yoghourt. Couple of glasses of red wine.

Sunday 11 October

Walk with Jinty before porridge breakfast. Also roll with butter and Ruth's home-made plum jam - couldn't leave that sitting in the jar to go mouldy! It was 2 o'clock before we had a roll and cold meat with a little celery-nut-apple salad and a glass of milk. In the evening there was roast pork with apple sauce, roasted root veg and broccoli. Apple-crumble with cream and yoghourt.

Monday 12 October

Breakfast of muesli with extra oats, then I fancied, and enjoyed, a roll with butter and chocolate hazelnut spread. I had an hour's drive to see a client, so made a peanut butter roll to eat in the car. On way home I felt the need to buy something for pudding for the evening so chose a toffee cake. Meal was pasta and roasted veg sauce, with extra mushrooms I found in the fridge. Then a slice of cake. Had a gin and tonic later with some Marmite rice cakes - then even later a glass of milk and slice of cake - just because it was there - looking at me.

Tuesday 13 October
Muesli and oats breakfast and I packed a box with salad and cottage cheese for my lunch. I also had a cup of lentil soup at work. Then by 3 o'clock I was in need of a cup of tea and a little something, so bought an apricot flapjack. It was very nice - but about 400 calories! Went to yoga straight from work so had cold pizza for my tea at 8 with a corner yoghourt. Had a little slice of the toffee cake before bed.

Wednesday 14 October
Muesli and oats breakfast. There won't be time for lunch today as I'm in the shop till 2 then have a client at 2.30. Had a quick tuna salad roll at 2 then back home 3-ish treated myself to a glass of milk and slice of cake. Dinner of

salmon with carrots, potatoes, broad beans and peas then small left over apple crumble with yoghourt.

Thursday 15 October
Muesli breakfast - work till 1 then a slice of cold pork and some couscous and pasta salad. Late evening meal of lamb chops, potatoes, carrot, turnip, leek, gravy and slice of cake - it's finished at last so will no longer be tempting me.

Friday 16 October
There's no doubt that boredom and idleness coupled with gluttony are a dangerous combination. Started well with muesli breakfast, tuna mayo salad roll and pea and ham soup for lunch but THEN I was offered a chunk of Cadbury's Dairy Milk, which I accepted. I then, of course, had to buy my own bar so that I could reciprocate. And they were on special offer in the shop - 2 for 70p instead of 55p each. So there's ANOTHER bar in my handbag ...Tea at Amy's - chilli with a wrap and rice. THEN chocolate cake and a biscuit. She'd made the biscuits so I had to try one. But why eat the unnecessary chocolate cake?? Because it's there. Fear of it being the last opportunity to eat chocolate cake? Crazy. Should I mention the glass of red wine?

As you begin to understand in what different ways you are urged to eat, it may be helpful to dig a little deeper and start writing out what happens to you on a day to day basis. If you photocopy the Daily Eating Journal at the back of this book, this will guide you through the following questions in more depth and when answered will help you identify more fully your main eating triggers. Each question requires a lot of thought and detailed information in order to uncover the many reasons we have for eating the way we do. Doing this exercise will allow you to get in touch with your thoughts, emotions and any physical sensations you might feel the next time you want to eat something.

KNOWING HOW TO IDENTIFY YOUR TRIGGERS

1. Why do I want to eat?

Think about why you eat, is it about how your stomach feels or how you are feeling in that moment or is it more about the environment you are in or perhaps you have a preoccupation with food, are always dieting and you feel deprived. Many people eat out of boredom, stress or in situations when they are not really hungry but something drives them to eat.

2. What do I eat?

In a day do you eat far too much and then feel guilty or perhaps starve yourself or just restrict your foods because that's what you always do. Do you eat fast foods, foods that are easy to prepare and junk foods? Are there any areas of your diet you feel are unhealthy? What specific foods do you eat when you are emotional, do you eat what your body needs, what your body wants or what you actually have in the cupboard? Do you drink alcohol if so why, how much, when do you drink, where, do you drink, do you drink on your own? Are there any particular changes you would like to make to your way of eating?

3. When do I eat, feel like eating?

Always ask yourself if you are really hungry when you want to eat something, what exactly is it that triggers that desire, how do you know? Then ask yourself how hungry you really are. Do you eat by the clock, when upset, for comfort, when alone? Are there any environmental cues that trigger your eating, perhaps you always eat something when you watch a particular TV programme, or you want to eat something every time you go into the kitchen, or you wait until you are starving and then eat too much and eat whatever you can lay your hands on. What could you do to help you deal with these particular eating patterns you have? What do you do to relax yourself?

4. Where am I when I want to eat?
Do you eat while watching TV, or while on the run, perhaps you eat in the car or at your office desk? Do you find you gulp your food and eat very quickly, are you alone while you eat, are you a secret eater sometimes feeling ashamed of what you are eating, or how much you are consuming in one sitting and prefer to do this alone where no-one will see you. Or do you prefer to eat with others, and if you do, do you eat differently when you are with other people? Think about all the different ways you eat and perhaps even begin to write these down just to remind yourself of what you do in different situations.

5. How do I feel before, during and after I eat?
Sometimes it can be difficult to pin point just what you are feeling. You might find this easier with the help of the "Feelings Bubbles" at the back of this book and it might help you decide just what you are feeling. Are you feeling, bored stressed, angry,

depressed, upset? Stop before you eat anything and take a deep breath and listen to your body. Ask yourself, what am I feeling? And then listen to the response, or notice where you are feeling something physically in your body, perhaps your stomach is churning, or your throat feels dry and tight or you have a tension headache, just try and get in touch with what you are feeling. Then when you begin eating the food try and get in touch with what you are feeling and where in your body you are feeling it. Again once you have eaten the food, how you feel then and if you feel any different to how you felt before you ate the food, and finally are you able to stop?

6. How much do I eat and how often?   Do you eat slowly or do you eat so quickly you don't even taste the food? Do you always clean your plate? Are you thinking of the food while you are eating it or is your mind on other things? Do you suffer from food cravings and find it really hard to stop once you start? How do you think you could change these eating patterns that would allow you to eat more slowly, think about what you are eating and stop eating when you feel full and eat only when you are truly hungry?

After discovering your main triggers for eating write them down in your Daily Eating Journal. Keep the journal at hand and over the next 3 months each time you eat anything write down firstly the trigger, what you ate, why you ate it, where you were and how you felt before during and after and describe in detail any situation or incident that was going on for you at that time. Doing this practice is the first step to becoming aware of what causes you to behave in a certain way. It will also help you understand why you do this and over time will be the catalyst for any changes you choose to make. Just by doing this and thinking about it will make a difference. If you find it easier just to think about it and if you would rather not write it down then that is fine, just do what feels right for you. Already you are on the road to becoming more mindful.

DAILY EATING JOURNAL

Keeping a Daily Eating Journal will allow you to work out the best ways to address your relationship with food. For best results you should begin the journal 2 weeks before you embark on your mindful eating journey. This will allow you to observe and record your different, patterns, behaviours and triggers to mindless eating which will then help you to implement the changes you want to make. It will also give you an insight into the possible reasons you behave in a certain way and what actions you need to take in order to change these.

Throughout the course of your mindful eating journey you can look back at what changes you have made and how your relationship with food has changed and whether mindful eating is working for you or not. It is useful to have the information written down as trying to remember what you have eaten from day to day can be challenging enough without also having to remember how you are feeling or what was going on for you at a particular time or day. Writing a food journal or diary can be time consuming and many of us can forget but it can really help you begin to understand and notice positive changes.

Research suggests that it takes 21 days to form a new habit. What you will find with writing everything down is that after a period of time you will begin to notice what is happening without actually writing it down. Becoming mindful and observing will eventually become second nature to you and you will find you no longer need to log everything. If you use the information below on how to identify your triggers, this will help you fill in the Daily Eating Journal and help you to recognise and notice any patterns that begin to develop or have already developed over time.

TIPS

♦ Fill out your daily eating diary every time you eat. This can be found at the back of the book. You may find you don't always remember to do this at first or you may be reluctant to do it but this will really help you in becoming more aware and mindful of just how you eat.

♦ Fill out your Feelings Journal each time you eat. This can be found at the back of the book. You can also write in your Feelings Journal when not eating. Having a diary of how you are feeling will really help you to get in touch with how you are feeling. It will help you understand if there are any particular feelings that trigger your eating patterns. Or you may well notice that when you are eating that certain feelings come and go throughout the eating activity. Again noticing and recording these feelings will allow you to see if there are any particular foods that cause you to feel a particular way or vice versa.

♦ If you find it hard to work out just how or what you are feeling use the Feelings Bubbles at the back of the book to help you.

♦ Start using some of the exercises and techniques already offered in the previous chapters. Like EFT or The Cloud technique. Both of these techniques offer completely different ways of changing how you feel.

ACTIVITY

What are your triggers?

Answering the following questions about your eating habits will give you some idea of your main triggers that form your eating patterns.

SITUATIONAL/ENVIRONMENTAL	Often	Sometimes	Seldom
1. Do you find you want to eat more when eating out in a restaurant, cinema etc?			
2. Are you easily tempted by images and smells of food such as buffet style displays or the smell of food cooking?			
3. Do you eat while watching TV, driving, while talking on the phone or reading a book?			
4. Do you eat because it is mealtime? E.g. when it's 12 o'clock even if not hungry?			
TOTAL			

Situational – If your answers fall mainly within this category then this might suggest that you are easily influenced by external influences such as eating while watching TV, while driving, always eating something while reading or you may also be thinking about what diet to try next. Food is probably never far from your thoughts as many different cues trigger your eating habits. Given the type of food climate we live in today it may be more challenging for someone in this category to try and avoid the many different cues to eat and find new ways to respond to such cues, especially to the ones which are difficult to avoid. Again as you begin to embrace the process of "Mindful Eating" you will find this less of a challenge. Some every day changes which may make a difference might be to change the way you buy, cook and serve food. Such as cooking from fresh, eating less ready made meals and "fast foods" and making changes to the environments you presently eat in. Or making a point of only eating in the kitchen, always sitting at a table to eat and having no distractions while you eat etc.

PHYSIOLOGICAL	Often	Sometimes	Seldom
1. Do you ever get headaches or feel particularly sluggish after eating certain foods?			
2. Do you ever want to eat when you feel physical pain or discomfort?			
3. Do you ever feel really hungry after you have eaten?			
4. Do you ever ignore your physical hunger pangs only to find yourself ravenous a few hours later and eating everything and anything you can find?			
TOTAL			

Physiological – If your answers fall mainly within this category then you may find you are eating to try and mask the physiological pain you are feeling. This may come from an experience you had in your childhood when you fell and hurt your knee and your mother offered you sweets to "make it all better". Or it may even come from a painful stomach problem and eating makes it feel less painful. Food intolerances can also make you eat in a certain way. Often people who crave certain foods like wheat, coffee, chocolate etc may be intolerant to that food. They may get headaches or feel particularly sluggish when they don't eat a particular food and this is relieved temporarily when they eat it. After eating that food the discomfort is relieved for a short while only to return again later. Many of us drink coffee because it gives us a bit of a "buzz" and temporarily heightens our sense of well-being and seems to "sharpen" our minds. Often, why you eat and what you eat can affect your eating behaviour.

If you don't eat at regular intervals and don't eat foods that will sustain you over time, then you may begin to suffer from low blood sugar which can result in trembling, shakiness and headaches. It is important to eat what your body needs at regular times throughout the day. With mindful eating you will begin to learn to listen and correctly interpret your body's physiological need for food.

EMOTIONAL	Often	Sometimes	Seldom
1. Do you ever find you want to eat more even after finishing a large meal?			
2. Do you ever eat when you nervous, upset or sad?			
3. Do you ever eat when you feel really happy or excited?			
4. Do you ever eat when you feel angry?			
TOTAL			

Emotional – If your answers fall mainly within this category then this shows that you are probably eating most of the time in response to how you feel, whether they are negative or positive feelings. Mindful eating is one way of addressing this and will help you to become more aware of what you are feeling at any given time or in any given situation and allow you to cope more effectively with these feelings. Instead of reaching out for food every time you feel a strong positive or negative feeling, you will learn that it is possible to react and respond differently. Developing new skills in how you deal with stress and how to communicate more effectively will also help.

THINKING	Often	Sometimes	Seldom
1. How often do you think about food?			
2. Do you ever give yourself a hard time for giving in and eating a "forbidden food"?			
3. Do you ever label or think of foods as "Good" or "Bad"?			
4. Do you often worry and continually criticize and judge yourself about how and what you eat?			
TOTAL			

Thinking – If your answers fall mainly within this category then the chances are that you will often find yourself consumed by the negative "mind chatter" that goes on in your head. This includes all the negative self talk, the beliefs you hold about yourself and others, past experiences and future expectations. Again as you begin to practice "mindful eating" and focus your mind in the moment, allowing any thoughts to come and go without attachment, judgment or criticism, then in time your "mind chatter" will become less and less. Try not to be such a perfectionist and be more flexible in your beliefs about the way things ought to be. Try not to be so hard on yourself and understand that we are all human beings doing our best. Try and appreciate that any negative thoughts, experiences or circumstances are giving you the opportunity to notice and learn more about yourself.

SOCIAL	Often	Sometimes	Seldom
1. Do you find it difficult not to overeat when you dine out?			
2. Do you believe you always have to clean your plate?			
3. Are you easily coerced into eating when you don't really want to?			
4. Do you ever use food as a reward for yourself or for others in your family?			
TOTAL			

Social – If your answers fall mainly within this category then this shows how vulnerable you are to the influences and pressures of your friends, family and other people. By improving your communication skills and learning to trust yourself will increase your self-confidence and allow you to make better decisions and choices. This will also help you to speak your truth and express yourself in a more open and honest way. Following the steps to self-acceptance in the next chapter and using the affirmations and mirror work discussed later on in the book will also help you feel more positive and self-assured about your self.

Add up your total scores for each different section. If your totals fall mainly within the "**often**" column of any section then these are the areas in your life that you need to look at. If your totals fall mainly within the "**sometimes**" column, then these areas in your life could well become problematic for you and you may want to take action to prevent this. If your totals fall mainly within the "**seldom**" column, then it sounds as if your relationship with food is relatively healthy.

When you calculate your scores for each section this will give you an indication of which areas are likely to trigger your eating. If most of the answers you have given have fallen within the "**often**" column in one or more of the different sections, then have a look below at each section to see which is relevant to you. This will help you understand what areas in your life impact on your relationship with food and offer different ways of how to deal with these day to day challenges in your life. Your answers don't need to fall within just one section, for example having two "**often**" answers in the Thinking Section and three "**often**" answers in the Emotional Section means that each of the questions within each different section are important areas to look at. If however you answer "**often**" to each question within one specific section then that particular section is strongly impacting on your relationship with food.

Many of the tips and exercises in the following chapters will also help to provide you with more ways of understanding and changing your eating triggers.

CHAPTER 8

Lord grant me the serenity to accept the things I cannot change,
the courage to change the things I can, and
the wisdom to know the difference."
(Saint Francis of Assisi)

SELF ACCEPTANCE

Complete self acceptance is not something that is easy to achieve. This is made even more unachievable by a society that attaches a great deal of importance to appearances and the relentless messages and images that we are presented with on a daily basis.

The first thing we have to do before we even consider practicing mindful eating is to learn self-acceptance. It is important to understand that self-acceptance only comes from within. Anything that makes you feel better that comes from outside yourself will only ever be temporary. Self-acceptance is about accepting who and what we are including all the negative thoughts and beliefs we have about ourselves and accepting all of ourselves without criticism or judgment. It is about total acceptance. Which may sound a little contradictory in relation to how we eat but it is about accepting all of ourselves which includes the labels of "good" and "bad" we have placed on our selves, our eating patterns and our behaviours. Understanding that it is both the "good" and the "bad" that makes us who we are and that no-one is perfect.

We are all here to learn and experience life in our own individual ways. What some of us have done is found ways of expressing ourselves through our relationship with food. It is not necessarily right or wrong, but it something we have found which has brought us to this point in our life's journey now. For all of us this is the right place for us to be in order to learn and progress with our journey. So although self acceptance is about accepting all of ourselves exactly as we are, we can still think our legs are too short or our nose is too big, or this cellulite looks so awful. It is about accepting every part of our selves whether a beautiful face or a big bum and understanding that this may change, or it may not, but right now, in this moment, this is how it is and accepting it.

When we apply this to mindful eating it means we really begin to get in touch with our body's needs. So instead of denying our bodies the food that they really need, we begin to listen to what our bodies tell us when we are hungry. After so many years of dieting and making ourselves feel guilty when we eat, it can sometimes take a little time for us to trust what our bodies are saying. Eating mindfully is about knowing and trusting that you are eating exactly what your body needs both in terms of nourishment and quantity. That whatever shape or size your body becomes through mindful eating, is exactly right for you and no amount of dieting is going to change that or make you feel any better about yourself. The secret lies in self-acceptance.

Steps to Self Acceptance

1. **Always think about yourself and encourage yourself**
2. **Get to know yourself**
3. **Be honest with yourself**
4. **Know that you are doing your best**
5. **Be aware of your inner critic**
6. **Let go and relax any judgments and criticisms**
7. **Praise yourself**
8. **Accept your feelings**
9. **Accept your differences**
10. **Work out what motivates you**

Body Image

So much of what we read about body image, how to look, what's acceptable, what's not acceptable tells us that we are not all right just as we are and that we need to do something in order to fit in, be accepted or look a certain way. What this implies is that the female body is an object and perhaps something to be perfected. Many things contribute to how a woman feels about her body. Peer pressure, family history, education, stage of life, and ethnic, cultural and social status all play important roles in how people feel about how they look. The media also massively influences body image.

We are overwhelmed by messages form the media about how we should look. This includes television, radio, billboards, magazines etc. Images of female bodies are everywhere and are used to sell everything and anything from food to cars. Many celebrities and actresses are singled out on a regular basis for either having lost too much weight or for having gained so much weight and this is usually accompanied by degrading and upsetting images of them spread over the front cover of a magazine or on a television programme. Again the message here is that unless you have the perfect body image you are not accepted and will be exposed and ridiculed for your inability to conform to what the media perceive as the perfect body image.

Today models are becoming taller, thinner and younger all the time. Many of the magazines we read are full of articles about different celebrities and how much weight they have gained or lost. We are also presented with very revealing and often distressing pictures of their weight gains or losses. It seems as though none of us can get it right according to the media or press. The message seems to be that if we can just attain this "perfect weight", we will be happy, we will get the perfect job we will get the perfect husband and will live happily ever after. These messages from the media impact on us very powerfully and over the years many of us have now begun to believe that unless we achieve this "perfect weight" or "perfect body image" then we will never achieve success and never find happiness.

Why are we not questioning why such unattainable and unrealistic standards of beauty are being imposed on women today? Generally speaking models are thinner and much taller than the average woman but what happens is that we internalize these stereotypes, and judge ourselves by the beauty industry's standards. By internalizing this ideal body shape and size we then start believing that if we can't quite make the grade then we will not be accepted. Perhaps the real reason behind this unattainable standard is more to do with the diet and beauty industry increasing their growth and profits but at the cost of developing a nation of women and men with a variety of eating disorders, distorted body image and mental health problems. Research suggests that depression and low self-esteem can be caused as a result of regular exposure to the perfect body image in both men and women. Here are a few tips to help you get on track and begin to accept yourself and all your beautiful imperfections that make you unique and exactly who you are, no matter what anyone else says.

Affirmations and Mirror Talk

Affirmations can be very powerful statements. The words you speak today create your tomorrows. We are all guilty of negative self-talk and our internal dialogue can often drive us crazy and cause us to be really hard on ourselves. As we frequently succumb to our incessant negative "mind chatter" we often find ourselves attaching to our thoughts, beliefs, judgements and feelings about ourselves, many of these being negative and self-deprecating such as, I am so fat, I hate myself when I eat too much, I am so ugly, I am afraid of this etc. This kind of self-talk is usually generated in your subconscious mind and most of the beliefs we are operating on today were formed in early childhood. By re-examining these outmoded thoughts and beliefs and replacing them with more positive statements we can bring lasting change to our lives.

Affirmations can be a very powerful way of breaking through your limiting thoughts and beliefs and can help to create new ways of thinking and can also bring about positive changes in our belief systems. Affirmations are usually made up of small but key positive messages to the self. They can be used in many situations throughout the day and help to remind us to stay positive. You may also find it even more powerful to write the affirmations out and leave them in various places throughout your home. Thinking, speaking and writing your affirmations out work really well together and are more powerful when combined. There is one other way to reinforce your affirmations and that is by looking at yourself in the mirror as you speak them.

Mirror Talk involves talking to your self in the mirror which many people find quite challenging at first. But this technique can be very empowering when practiced every day. Choose an affirmation and then practice this for at least 21 days. You may get emotional and upset at first or feel uncomfortable because you are not used to loving yourself or having compassion for yourself. Given time this will change and you will begin to feel quite differently about yourself.

If you feel too uncomfortable initially using the mirror work you can write out a few different affirmations and place them in useful places throughout your home. It is always better to devise your own affirmation based on what you think and feel about yourself but the following list may just give you a little help. One other very powerful way to use affirmations is by devising them yourself, recording them and then listening to them through headphones as you go about your daily chores, while driving to work or just before you go over to sleep at night or really just at a time to suit yourself. If you follow the instructions in the activity section on "how to create affirmations" this will help you devise your own which will be much more powerful than using someone else's.

TIPS

♦ Stop weighing yourself. Your weight is not important. It is only an indicator of how heavy you are. It says nothing about your body shape, body build or your genetic tendencies. If you are doing exercises and toning up your muscles, you will begin to weigh heavier. Muscle weighs heavier than fat and the more toned you become the faster you will burn fat thus increasing your weight and reducing inches.

♦ Think twice before buying Fashion and Beauty Magazines. Fashion and Beauty Magazines will only make you feel ugly and inferior. The images that are presented to us in the majority of magazines are false. Have you ever come across a magazine showing your average looking girl with spots and pimples, cellulite, crooked nose, fat bum, thunder thighs etc....NO!, and that's because images can often be airbrushed or changed in some way. When we are continually presented with pictures of the "Perfect Body Image" we become convinced that unless we can look like this then we are inferior, less than perfect and therefore not acceptable. Very few people can live up to this image. Understand and believe that you are perfect as you are, you are an intelligent, attractive woman with imperfections that make you unique and interesting no matter what age or body shape you are.

♦ Honour your uniqueness. We are all different in so many ways, enjoy your differences because there will never be anyone just like you. Treat yourself with as much care and understanding as you would others, accept compliments, take responsibility for the choices you make and live your life with purpose.

♦ Never compare yourself to others. It can be hard not to compare yourself to others but is really quite pointless. You are what you are and you will always come across people you think are more attractive, prettier, thinner or more successful than you. Judging others on their appearance, status and accomplishments is only part of who they are. Your judgments of them are also part of who you are. See yourself and others as complex, interesting and unique human beings who all have something wonderful to offer. When you stop judging yourself you will stop judging others.

♦ Stop looking in the mirror. How many times during the day to you check your reflection in the mirror? Make a decision to check yourself only once every day. If you find this difficult, then at least be kind to the person looking back at you. So many of us obsess and check ourselves in mirrors, shop windows, anywhere really we can see our reflections. In what way does this make you feel good about yourself? If you make a conscious effort to cut down on your mirror checking, you may well be surprised to find you feel a whole lot better about your body image.

♦ Focus on your strengths. What kind of things are you good at, when do you feel really passionate and inspired and what do you do best? In what way are you different to others? Just think about what you bring to your life and the lives of others, are you particularly good with people or do you prefer working with animals? Perhaps you are really good with numbers or are really good at singing or playing an instrument. Take some time to reflect on this and as you do you will release that you are so much more than your physical body. Just for a moment imagine you and the whole of humanity were blind, how would that change how you feel about yourself and others?

♦ Begin to live more consciously. The more you recognize how precious human life is and that our physical bodies are really only a vehicle to see us through this life, the more you will become less self-focused and less body-obsessed. Paying more attention to everything and becoming more mindful of your thoughts will really help you get in touch with what is real and what is not, what is important and what is not.

♦ Show gratitude. Start a Gratitude Log and write down all the things you are grateful for in your life. According to research expressing and practicing gratitude is good for you and promotes health, inspires success and helps you sleep better. The more positive things you focus on in your life the more joy you will bring to it. Helping others can be a great way to make you feel better about yourself and lift your spirits. Placing your focus on the positive things in your life and what you are grateful for will draw even better things to you.

♦ Meditate Daily. Meditation can bring balance and relaxation to your life. As you become more relaxed you will find that you are much more able to deal with life's daily ups and downs. Meditation will help you begin to understand the power of the mind/body connection and by changing your thoughts and your beliefs will help change how you feel about your body image.

ACTIVITY
How to create Affirmations

When you create affirmations it is important to create positive affirmations. For example it is better to say "I am calm and relaxed" rather than "I have no stress". When you use the word "no" your subconscious mind doesn't understand or recognize the word "no" or "yes" therefore the interpretation will then be "I have stress" and your mind will then focus on stress with the likely result of creating MORE stress. Creating affirmations is about focusing on what you **do** want rather than on what you **do not** want. It is more effective if your affirmations have action verbs and/or positive emotions. For example "I love myself" or "I really enjoy singing and I am good at it" You could even make up a little song or poem and recite this back to yourself.

It is also important to keep your affirmations short and sweet. The reason for this is because you're sending a message to your subconscious mind rather than your conscious mind and the more complex the statement the more likely your subconscious mind will not receive it. For example "I love and accept myself" or "I am really confident" are short and simple statements. Using words that are negative or that suggest you might fail are also not good to use such as, "I will try to do my best" or "I hope I can change". If these types of words are used then change will be highly unlikely. Something like "I always do my best" or "I can change", are much more effective. Repeating the affirmation regularly throughout the day will embed that statement in your subconscious mind and this eventually becomes your reality.

Affirmations are also time sensitive and it is necessary to keep your affirmations in the present tense. For example if you were to affirm "I will be really happy when I pass my exam" that would suggest that you are not happy now and you will only be happy in the future. The purpose of affirmations is to allow you to change any thoughts or beliefs that no longer serve you in your present life into something else that does not exist in your life at the moment. No matter what your intention is, with the right affirmations expertly crafted, you WILL change. If you repeat your affirmations each day, probably morning and evening is best then eventually they will become a regular part of your thinking and your life will begin to change. You may well begin to notice a number of changes happening as you begin to practice and incorporate affirmations into your daily routine, like an increase in confidence, your relationships improving, fear and negativity become a way of the past and you start believing in your self.

CHAPTER 9

"Every intention sets energy into motion
whether you are conscious of it or not."
(Gary Zukav)

GOALS AND INTENTIONS

How much you want something is usually determined by how motivated you are to really achieve what you want and is usually driven by some form of internal or external need. So if you want to change your relationship with food then you have to take action. Having goals in your life is important but setting and having goals is something that is usually based on some future outcome. If you do want to change something then you do need to take action but it is more about taking that action now and creating and focusing on what you want now rather than at some point in the future. If you try to create something for the future you are likely to begin to have doubts and fears about whether you can achieve it or not and you may well begin to attach beliefs and feelings to the outcome. Such as "I will feel really happy when I have achieved my goal" What this suggests is that you are not happy right now and that you are chasing happiness, chasing your dreams. It is not about how you will feel at some time in the future it is more about how you feel now and how you pursue your goal. If you continually live with your mind set at some place in the future then you will never be happy or content with what you have right now. So although goals can help us with direction and taking action, they are very much based on a future outcome.

Intentions on the other hand are much more about what matters to us and bring our actions in line with our values. Intentions are much more about how we are being in the present moment and are supported by our integrity. Intentions help us move forward towards our goal, they come from within and are more about how we feel and how we listen to our gut feelings. Goals on the other hand are more about what we think and are based on some future expectation. Our intentions are what we feel deep down and how we express ourselves in our daily lives and this is what creates our vision. Goals are more the external result of what we have internally created. Just thinking about your goal and writing it down is not enough, you have to be what you desire. See it, feel it, hear it, believe it and live it right now.

By mindfully creating your intention (what you focus on) you create the outcome you have focused on. So if your goal is to earn £5000 every month for the rest of your life and you continue to focus on how poor you are or how you never have any money, then the outcome is not likely to be £5000 every month, nothing is likely to change. Having a goal that is not aligned with your larger beliefs can result in your intentions undermining your goals. By aligning your intentions with your larger beliefs and passions will allow you to reach your goals much more easily and with less effort.

Intention is the driving force and power behind your goals and what you want to create in your life. By positively setting intentions and taking the necessary action required to achieve them, you will begin to notice the pleasure and enjoyment in working towards what you want especially if these are some of the intentions you set. We all want to achieve things in our lives. Just notice your attitude and how you go about it as that can determine how much you enjoy the experience.

The most challenging part of setting an intention is to set it and then let it go. What so many of us often do is think or imagine something will develop or manifest in a particular way. When we do this we are holding on to what we expect to happen. Yes it is really important to feel it, visualize it etc but then let it go and accept that whatever comes back to you and in whatever form is exactly as it should be for you. What so many people do is imagine **how** this will happen or imagine **how** they want it to happen. If you do that then expect to be disappointed.

An example of this might be deciding that you are only going to eat when you are physically hungry. If you do that then the chances are you are going to fail. Perhaps just becoming aware of your thoughts or getting in touch with your feelings or what you are feeling physically would be a smaller more realistic way of moving towards your end goal of only eating when you are physically hungry. The whole point of mindful eating is about accepting whatever is happening in that moment without judgment or criticism. Yes by all means set your self a long term goal but remember to be patient, kind, gentle and compassionate with yourself. Make your goals realistic, set your intentions for each day and if you don't quite get there, don't beat yourself up about it. The more accepting you can be of yourself and the more honest you can be with yourself as you go through this new process of change the faster you will begin to see the changes happening.

Here are some examples of how you might set your intention for the day:

Each morning as you get up, begin to think about the day ahead and write down or say what you intend that day to be like. How do you intend to feel? What impact do you intend to have? Notice how this changes your day.

Your intention for one day might be to decide to really listen to your thoughts and feelings and write them down in your journal throughout the day.

Another intention might be to eat alone, sitting down in the kitchen with no sounds or distraction and then to record your thoughts and feelings about that meal in your Daily Eating Journal.

TIPS

♦ Start small. Begin with something easy and achievable and then grow and develop other goals from there. For example if your goal is to develop a healthy relationship with food, then it might be easier to break that down into bite sized pieces. Perhaps your intention for each day for the next week might be something like observing yourself while eating one item of food like a piece of fruit or a biscuit every day for the next week. Just be in the moment for the time it takes to eat that food. Then after a week you can increase this to watching and observing yourself while you eat breakfast each day for the next week. Then you can set your next intention and so on and so forth until you achieve your desired outcome.

♦ One Goal. Too many people start with too many goals at once, and try to do too much. This can wear you down and reduce you motivation. People often make this mistake. Trying to focus on more than one thing at a time means that each goal does not achieve the energy and focus that is necessary for it to be achieved in all its' totality.

♦ What's your motivation? Know exactly why you are doing it, what your reasons are and what you need to do to achieve it. It can often help if you write your reasons down. Always do it for something that you really, really want to happen, for really good reasons and do it for you. If you try to do it for someone else then it won't work.

♦ Really want it. When you set a goal it is no good just wanting it, you need to feel passionate about it, feel inspired when you think about it, something you really want in your life or a change in your lifestyle. You really need to be what you want. For example if you never want to diet again and want to change your relationship with food then there is no point in dreaming about how this will look when you have achieved it. You need to start taking action now and be what you want now.

♦ Be in the moment. If you really want to develop a healthy relationship with food, imagine how you will feel when you have achieved this, how you will look, how happy you will be, what a difference this change will make to your life, not feeling controlled by food and never having to say to people you are on a diet, saying that yes I can eat whatever I like whenever I want. All these thoughts and feelings are in the future, what you need to do now is bring them into the present and feel and be exactly what you want now.

♦ Be inspired. Visualise what you want in rich detail using colour, clarity and where you see this (location). Putting feeling into what you want makes it feel so much more real. Imagining the feeling is no different to visualisation other than the fact that you are using a different sense. Act as if, imagine it is really happening. The mind doesn't know the difference between imagination and reality. Act and feel how fantastic it is to have what you desire right now and believe it! Talk to others about it, read about what you want to achieve and how you would like it to be. Once you have done all that it is just a matter of carrying that energy and enthusiasm forward and keeping it going.

♦ Write it down. Write down your daily intentions and your long term goal using large print/letters. Make your goal short and succinct, just a few words long, a bit like an affirmation and visualize this on a regular basis. Post it in places that will remind you to continue to focus your mind on it. It helps to have reminders like written words or pictures in different places.

ACTIVITY
Mindful Eating Visualisation

This visualization is something that can be done just prior to eating or preparing a meal. It will help you get in touch with what you are really feeling and how to be more focused as you prepare and eat your food.

Find your self a quiet comfortable place to sit, close your eyes and just relax. Begin by inhaling deeply drawing your breath up from the base of your naval and slowly exhale gently expelling all the air in your lungs. Do this 3 more times and with each inhale imagine all your mindless activities of the day being gently pulled up through your body and out of the top of your head. Continue to relax and watch as small clouds begin to form above your head, imagine each one is a different colour and inside each cloud you notice all your troubles of your day slowly floating away far into the distance. Now you are ready to prepare your first mindful meal.

As you walk into your kitchen, pay close attention to the surroundings, the decor and the ambience being created within this room. Take time to prepare your food and set your table. Place a few fresh flowers out the garden on the table and use your favourite dinner plates to lay the table and begin to generate a gentle and relaxing atmosphere.

Think about the food you are preparing, how and where it has come from. Understand that food is a gift of mother earth and the whole universe and without it we would not be able to nourish our bodies and survive. Imagine how it was grown, who grew it, how much effort was put into growing it and what conditions the animals or livestock were reared in. When you are ready to begin your food preparation, really pay attention to the food, touch it, smell it, take in the variety of colours and vibrancy of each food and accept what food you have with gratitude.

As you sit down at your carefully prepared table and meal, notice if you have the urge to eat as you look at the food on your plate, is your mouth watering, is your stomach rumbling? Notice what you are feeling, where are you feeling it in your body. Be aware of any thoughts that arise, just notice them and let them go. Put a bite in your mouth. Notice how the food feels in your mouth, is it smooth, or is it crunchy, how does it taste, sweet, salty, savoury or perhaps it's bland. Is it hot or cold, raw or cooked, how does it smell?

Use all your senses to really appreciate the food you are eating. Be aware of any emotions that arise and notice where you feel them in your body. As you continue to eat alone and in silence with no form of distraction or conversation, be aware of how different this experience is and take your time.

Before you swallow, notice the things that happen in your mouth when you put food in. Notice how you salivate, notice the urge to swallow, notice the sensation of chewing. As you swallow your food, notice what it feels like as you push the food to the back of your mouth with your tongue.

As your stomach receives the food, how does it feel? Is it relaxed or tight, perhaps you are feeling anxious or sad or angry. As you continue to eat, how does your stomach feel as it becomes a little fuller? Continue to enjoy and savour each bite until you feel full and satisfied. Only eat what your body wants, don't eat until your plate is empty, really listen to your body and get in touch with the feelings of fullness in your stomach. Now take a large deep breath and slowly open your eyes. You are ready to prepare a wonderful mindful meal. Notice if you feel any different while preparing and eating this meal.

CHAPTER 10

"You have to leave the city of your comfort and go into the wilderness of your intuition. What you'll discover will be wonderful. What you'll discover is yourself."
(Alan Alda b.1936)

7 STEPS TO MINDFUL EATING

If we want to be able to live life more fully and vibrantly, we need to be more mindful in our actions and choices and this includes what we choose to eat. Dieting is restrictive and cannot be sustained over time. It leaves us feeling guilty and disappointed that we have failed. This chapter will guide you through the 7 simple steps that will transform the way you eat. You will learn how to get in touch and listen to your body and how it communicates with you. You will learn how to trust yourself. Knowing what to eat, when to eat and how much to eat will become effortless and easy. You will begin to recognize what triggers you have and how you can overcome these and finally how to balance eating for health with eating for pleasure without any form of deprivation or guilt.

Make each bite count

In the moment

Notice what's happening inside and outside your body and observe everything

Don't judge or criticize or try to change anything
Full awareness and attention
Unconditional love and self-compassion
Let go

1. Make each bite count. Use all your senses. When you begin to eat, really experience everything about the food the way it looks, how it is presented, how it feels in your hand if you are able to touch it, the smell of the food, the taste of the food, the multiple flavours, the texture of the mixture of food in your mouth, the heat or coolness of it. Really focus on every single aspect of the food. Observe the sensation of taste, does it reduce after a few bites, are the flavours just as strong at the end of the meal as they were at the beginning. Notice each bite and how much you put in your mouth, do you stuff it full or do you just take small amounts. Is your plate overflowing or is there still room for more. As you become less hungry notice how full your stomach is, do you still have stomach hunger or are you satiated, or have you eaten until your stomach feels tight and uncomfortable.

Learning how to tell the difference between full and satisfied is something that can be quite confusing as you begin to eat more mindfully. If you miss the cues your body is sending you, you will overeat. Many of us think or believe that we must clean our plates. We may have been brought up being told that if we don't finish everything on our plates then we won't get a dessert or pudding, or you can't leave the table until you clean your plate. These kinds of memories and beliefs stick with us and can be hard to change. The wonderful thing about mindful eating is that by stopping when you are satisfied rather than full, means that you can eat again as soon as you become hungry. There are no rules in mindful eating, you are completely free to choose when and what you eat by listening to your body. You are not bound by any rules or by someone dictating when or how much you should or shouldn't eat.

Often before we begin the Monday morning ritual of "I'm starting my diet today", we have already set ourselves up to fail yet again. Sunday night, the night before the diet begins we have gone into deprivation mode, knowing that we will be deprived of all the foods we love. Our response..."let's binge on all the foods we love, because we won't be able to eat them again for ages", so we settle down for the night in front of the TV with huge amounts of all our favourite foods. This would normally include copious amounts of, chocolate, crisps, cheese, cream cakes etc, and we often eat until we feel sick. It is the denial that creates the craving. The more you allow yourselves the foods you crave the less you will crave them and eventually eliminate them or eat them in s mindful way. This is what the mind does when it believes it is going to be deprived. Wouldn't you prefer to feel free to eat whatever you want as and when you feel hungry? Wouldn't that give you much more pleasure than stuffing yourself to bursting point with foods you love through fear that you will be completely deprived of them over the course of your new diet or until you "fail" and give in to your cravings. With mindful eating you never feel deprived, you never need to binge, you are in control, you decide when to eat, what to eat and how much to eat. If you just listen to your body's needs, there will be no need to deprive yourself and with mindful eating there are no rules to stick to and no-one saying what you should or shouldn't be eating.

Something you might find quite scary as you begin to ponder the possibility that mindful eating might just be right for you is portion size! Yikes you might be saying," I can't possibly be let loose or allowed to eat as much as I want. I might die from eating so much and my belly might explode from the sheer quantity of food I am stuffing in there." This is not a problem if you are eating mindfully. If you are listening to your body as you eat and you are conscious of how full and how satisfied you are becoming as you eat. You will stop when your body tells you. Okay, I hear you asking..."But what about when I first begin, I won't know how to listen or what the signs are" Again this is nothing to concern yourself about your body is a very clever piece of machinery and has a number of different ways of telling you, that you are full and satisfied. Yes in the beginning you may miss the cues, you may start eating mindfully but give up half way through or initially you may just eat what you want mindlessly. Trust yourself, be patient with yourself, be kind to yourself and eventually over time you will begin to notice and become aware of what you are feeling and sensing and eat in a more enjoyable and mindful way.

2. In the moment. There's no-one better at being present or eating intuitively than a child. Children are not thinking about what happened to them yesterday, or what they are going to do later today. They are here in the moment fighting, playing, laughing eating, singing, and nothing else in the world exists. If they get mad about something, they can overreact but nothing else in the world matters but what has upset them. They will cry about it, and then soon return to normal, happy again, the offending situation forgotten without a grudge. They have no cares about yesterday, tomorrow, next year or whenever. We need to use children as inspiration, and try to be like them sometimes. If you watch babies and children you will see that they intuitively eat the right food and the right amount. They listen to the information their bodies are giving them and respond accordingly.

Do you eat while reading? If so, you might have noticed that sometimes you can eat an entire meal without even really tasting the food. This applies to a lot of things in our lives. We can spend an hour with our family without really talking to them. We can go to a park or the beach, and not really notice the things around us.

First of all think about what you normally do when you eat something. Do you sit in front of the TV, is the radio blaring, are you on the phone, are you thinking about your next meal, planning your next holiday in your head....**STOP!** Here's a tip that seems so simple, and yet can be difficult to maintain in practice...be present in your mind and with your body. Turn the TV off and go into another room, turn the radio off, take the phone off the hook, bring your mind into the present and just be still. Ask yourself if you are really hungry and be very careful to listen to what your body tells you. If the answer is yes and you are ready to eat, then go right ahead and eat.

Initially you may find it hard to work out what your body is telling you and how to determine true physical hunger signals as opposed to emotional hunger or some other form of hunger, but this will begin to change over time. Don't beat yourself up if you suddenly find yourself saying" Stuff what my body says I feel a craving coming on and I really need to satisfy this urge to eat chocolate" Go right ahead, the fact that you are recognizing what is happening means that you are in the moment and becoming aware of your feelings and behaviour, and that in itself is progress. The more you are able to stop, breathe and just listen for a moment the more likely you will be able to really listen to what your body is telling you.

3. Notice everything. What's happening inside and outside your body and observe everything Just watch from moment to moment every thought that arises in your mind. When difficult thoughts arise, just watch and in time you will learn to witness rather than obey them and get caught up in the mindless mind chatter that goes on in all our heads. In time you will begin to realise that your thoughts and feelings aren't really who you are. They come and they go, and if you don't react and attach to them, they begin to lose their power. You can learn how to be with your experience, but not be caught up in it.

Over time and with practice you will begin to improve your witnessing ability and begin to notice when you are being habitual rather than mindful. Having this awareness will help overcome these destructive pattern and behaviours. You will begin to understand what it feels like not to become attached and bogged down with the belief that you are whatever you are feeling and thinking. Eventually, as you begin to accept your uncomfortable feelings and thoughts with compassion, without the need to deny them. You may find that you no longer feel the need to bury them with a deluge of cream cakes, chocolate or chips.

What we eat and how we eat are also influenced by external factors such as, the environment, social triggers, friends, peers, advertising, food packaging and so on. People can be very impressionable when it comes to how much they will eat. For example you may be out shopping for some clothes or accessories and bump into a friend, she suggests going for a coffee so that you can both catch up. You excitedly agree and when you get there end up ordering a large café latte and a huge chocolate muffin, just because that's what people do when they go to coffee shops. You haven't seen your friend in ages and this is something you always used to do together while catching up. You think you have been "good" this week on your diet and think you deserve a "treat". Your friend has also ordered cake and coffee and is sitting there demolishing a big piece of strawberry gateau.

Unless you can step back and bring awareness to the situation, yes go for a coffee but be mindful as you order, stop and listen to what your body needs. Don't just wade right in there and join the throngs of people in the café as they sit and chat while mindlessly eating large cakes and doughnuts. It is absolutely fine to have whatever you want and in whatever quantity, hot chocolate, big cream cakes, doughnuts, muffins and so on but take stalk for one minute prior to ordering and just get in touch with what your body needs and listen! If you are eating as a treat then you will most likely eat far too much. If you are eating your muffin and drinking your latte because you always do this with this particular friend, then you are eating out of habit or association. If you are ordering and eating without getting in touch with your senses, then you are eating mindlessly.

By practicing mindful eating you will also notice an increase in your confidence, as you begin to believe in yourself and trust your intuition knowing when you are eating mindfully or when you are out of control and eating mindlessly. Awareness gives you the choice of continuing to be controlled or not by how you feel or what you think and this choice gives you a sense of freedom. The freedom to choose, gives belief and hope that change is possible.

4. Don't judge or criticize. Observing without judgment or criticism while eating and drinking is no easy feat. This involves noticing your feelings and thoughts about your food as you eat and all the other activities you have come to associate with eating in general. Observe them as they arise and then let them go. Our thoughts and feelings are not who we are, they are transient and will pass. They have nothing to do with the food you are eating or about to eat. If you suddenly find yourself in an eating frenzy, like shoving scoopfuls of ice cream into your mouth, just stop and notice what you are doing. Notice everything about it, where you are, what you are doing, what you are feeling etc, and if judgment or criticism arise which they undoubtedly will, then allow them to be there too. Be kind with yourself, this is just one moment, feelings come and go, can be pleasant or unpleasant and will eventually pass.

Many of us label food "Good" or "Bad" or we might even say "I have been good today, I haven't cheated and I have stuck to my diet". On the other hand we might say "I have been so bad today, I have eaten nothing but "bad" food. So already we are judging ourselves on our performance and behaviour and labelling food as "good or "bad". There is no such thing as "good food" and there is no such thing as "bad food". Every food has some form of nutritional benefit for each and every one of us. The reason we label these foods as such is because we have come to rely on them and have found some sort of comfort and escape from our feelings and emotions when we eat them. We have continually deprived ourselves of these foods over long periods of time believing that they are "bad" and will make us fat, but find them so tempting and so delicious. We feel unable to resist the temptation to eat them and then when we do give in to their temptation and eat them, we feel out of control and unable to stop ourselves and proceed to eat them in copious amounts. The foods we label as "bad" are often high in fat and sugar which we are told is unhealthy and should only be eaten in small quantities. The more we deprive ourselves of our favourite foods, the more we crave them and the more we do something we believe is wrong and bad, the more we continue to judge and criticize ourselves.

Food is only food and the only reason it becomes something more is because of the power we give it through our limiting thoughts and beliefs. As you continue the process of mindful eating you will begin to let go the need to judge or criticize yourself or the foods you eat knowing that you can eat any food in any quantity in any way, shape or form that you so desire. Giving yourself permission to eat anything you want when you are hungry is really quite scary but makes it much easier to really know exactly what that food is. You may find that you don't always want to eat chocolate, cakes, or sweets and that you are just as capable of choosing fruits or vegetables. It is just a matter of learning to trust that the choices you make are perfect for you in that moment.

5. Full awareness and attention There are so many different ways we can be distracted when we eat and there are so many habits we have formed over the years which influence our eating patterns and styles. The diet industry has brainwashed us into believing that we are incapable of making our own decisions and choices about what, where, how, why and when we eat. Each time we start a new diet we are flooded with information about what we can and cannot do and what we can and cannot eat believing that the experts know best. We have also learnt to eat according to the time of day, often being told that there are only particular times of the day when we can eat whether we are hungry or not, with little or no provision made for anyone who naturally gets hungry at another time. What this has done is to teach us how to suppress all our natural cues to eat and this has eventually caused us to lose our ability to get in touch with our own senses.

To eat with full awareness you need to get in touch with your body and listen to how and what it is trying to communicate to you. For example when you feel tired, your body begins to slow down, your eyes want to close, you may yawn and experience feelings of weakness and lethargy. If you listen correctly to those signs, you will rest your body and may even fall asleep. If you have wrongly associated these feelings in the past with needing to eat, and believing your body is weak with lack of food and hunger then unless you really become aware of how your body communicates with you then you may continue to mistake the feeling of tiredness for hunger.

When you experience true physiological hunger you usually feel hunger pangs and your stomach feels empty and makes rumbling noises. Some people can and do feel weak and tremble due to low blood sugar, which can be a sign that we need to eat or may be a sign of a specific medical condition. Often low blood sugar can be due to an imbalanced diet often high in unrefined sugars. When we begin to eat with awareness and trust our intuition our diets start to change and become more balanced and healthy as you listen to what your body needs preventing any nutritional imbalance which might result in a low blood sugar.

As your awareness develops and you become more attentive to your body's needs you will begin to notice that you are able to get back in touch with your senses and listen to your body's cues telling you what you are hungry for and when you have had enough. This is what having a healthy balanced relationship with food, is all about. Trusting yourself to eat when you are hungry, eating what you want and knowing when you are satisfied and full.

6. Unconditional love and self-compassion. How we relate to food can often be reflected in how we relate to other people or even to ourselves. Consider the relationships you have in your life right now and what they are saying about you and your relationship with food or even the relationship you have with yourself. Can you see any similarities? Yo-yo dieters and anyone who has spent any length of time trying to attain a particular weight or size will recognize in themselves that this has had a detrimental effect on how they feel about themselves. Many of us can and do use food for a variety of reasons, not just because we are hungry. Often our reasons are because of how we feel about ourselves or because of habits and behaviours we have adopted over the years that have allowed us to cope, helped us feel safe or have enabled us to deny or suppress our feelings and emotions. All sorts of eating disorders and behaviours can develop as a result of this. Many of these behaviours can be caused by how we feel about ourselves and over time this can develop into low self worth, low self-esteem, lack of confidence etc and many of us believe ourselves to be unworthy and unlovable.

When developing a practice of mindful eating it is important to have compassion for yourself as this helps to decrease the self criticism and emotional distress that fuels emotional eating. Be kind to yourself, understand that when you suffer or fail that this is all part of being human and be patient with yourself. Becoming mindful and learning new behaviours takes time and commitment. Your feelings will come and go, just be aware of them, don't judge or criticize them, just accept them for what they are in that moment.

Being self-compassionate is about noticing when you are suffering and responding to your pain with warmth and caring. It is about understanding and knowing that you are doing your best. It is about realizing that you are not perfect and will fail at times and that you're suffering is all part of being human. Having compassion for your self is really no different than having compassion for others. Self-compassion is about noticing when you are having a difficult time, or when you see something in yourself that you don't like or when you behave in a way you feel is unacceptable. Instead of giving yourself a hard time, or ignoring your suffering, stop and tell yourself " I am finding this so difficult right now", what can I do to nurture and care for myself in this moment? All too often we beat ourselves up for not being good enough, we wish parts of our bodies were different or that we were more attractive. Instead of judging and criticizing yourself for any inadequacies or shortcomings why not try to be more understanding of your self when confronted with personal failings.

Life is a roller coaster, that's what makes it so exciting. We are all different, some people are funny, some are serious, and some people are tall, while others are small. Variety is what makes life so interesting and different and all our differences make us completely unique human beings. There is only one you and there will never ever be anyone exactly like you again.

Becoming more self compassionate will help you understand and honour your uniqueness. It is important to only change in ways that allow you to be more healthy and happy, but only doing so because you care about yourself and not because you believe you are unacceptable or worthless as you are. Life is changeable and things will not always stay the way they are, you will make mistakes, you will fall short of your ideals and you may not always like how you feel but this is reality, this is what being human is all about and each one of us has to experience it in our own way. The more open and accepting you can be to this way of being, rather than fighting against it, the more loving and compassionate you will become with your self and everyone else.

7. Let Go. Much of our pain and suffering is not caused by our experiences but by our need to hold on to them in ways that do not benefit us in any way. In other words we form unhealthy attachments to our thoughts and feelings believing that this will benefit us in some way. Rather than accept that we have had an experience or we thought or felt a certain way and move on from that, we want to keep it as it is, or we make ourselves believe that it was different from how it really was and hold on to that. One of the secrets to relieving our pain and suffering is to let go our attachments and be in the moment. Continuing to hold on to these painful thoughts and feelings means we are not living in the present. As long as we dwell in the past or live in the future we cannot be present in this moment. When we learn to do this, then and only then will we are free from much of our pain and suffering.

Look back at how your mindless eating began or your binge eating or your unhealthy relationship with food started. What was the trigger or what were the triggers, was it a thought, a feeling or an experience. Perhaps it was your parents, did they always tell you to clean your plate, did they try to placate you with food to make them feel better or did they try to control what ever you ate. Perhaps it was more to do with your peers, were they all skinny and you were average weight and size and because you didn't fit in with their image of "normal" they all called you "fatty". What can happen as a result of this is that we then hold on to all these painful thoughts, memories and experiences and continue to torture ourselves on a regular basis remembering, replaying and reliving them in our minds.

The relationship we have with food now is often a reflection of what our thoughts, feelings, beliefs and experiences have been throughout our lives. It can often be confused with how we feel about ourselves and can be used to help us cope with our feelings and emotions. How our relationship with food was formed can be very similar to how we have formed the many other relationships in our lives.

Food is not the enemy although many of us would like to think it is. If you have continually been on and off diets throughout your life, you may now have formed the belief that you must control what you eat at all costs, you must deny yourself the pleasure of eating what you want when you want for fear of losing control and gaining weight. This has been your experience for so long that you no longer trust yourself and can't believe that you would ever be able to trust yourself to eat without gaining weight. Letting go of this belief will give you the freedom to choose and trust your intuition, allowing you to make the choices that your body needs bringing back the desire and pleasure associated with eating.

Letting go the belief that certain foods are "good" and certain foods are "bad" can also bring relief and allow you to break free of the craving cycle that so many Yo-Yo dieters experience throughout their lives. The more you deny yourself a food, the more you crave it. Try eating one food you crave madly for a whole day? Watch what happens? Did you last the whole day? At what point did you feel sick?

Another way to help you let go your cravings is to make sure you always keep plenty of your most craved foods in the house. When you get the urge, go through the process of stop, breathe and listen and if you can't seem to get in touch with any feeling and still have the urge. Then set whatever you have out on a plate, 10 Mars Bars, 20 Kit-Kats, a whole bowl of peanuts, a whole bowl of crisps...whatever your craving is. Make sure you remove all the wrappers of the Mars Bars and Kit-Kats, open all the peanuts and crisps and put them in a bowl or on a plate, sit down and enjoy! Observe what is happening, watch your thoughts, what you are feeling as you plough through your Kit-Kats, don't judge yourself or criticize, just accept that is what you are doing in this moment. You may well be surprised at how few you do eat, but whether you eat 2 or 22, it doesn't matter, you have done it as mindfully as you could in that moment.

Mindful eating is all about becoming aware of the reasons we eat mindlessly and how we can change this. This way of eating puts you in control and opens up your awareness, allowing you to get in touch with what is really happening in your mind and body. Listening to yourself in this way allows you to be present and really sense what your body needs or what your feelings are communicating, be it food, love, understanding, exercise and so on. Being present and mindful lets you eat only what your body needs...no more, no less.

Each time you think about eating whether it is a snack or a meal it may be useful to fill out your Daily Eating Journal. Fill it in using as much information and detail as possible, perhaps noting things like what events have been occurring in your life at this time and how these events have been making you feel and behave while also making use of your hunger score chart and feelings chart. This will help you recognise how hungry you were and what or how you were feeling at the time. Keeping a detailed journal like this will really help you follow you're eating pattern and may help you work out any triggers or habits you have developed over the years.

TIPS

As you begin to practice mindful eating things to look out for:

♦ Initially you may find it difficult to evaluate the different kinds of hunger. This may take time to develop but eventually you won't even have to think about it, you will just know.

♦ At first you may want to eat so much of what you have continually denied yourself over the years. This is quite normal. Just be aware of it, don't judge yourself as eventually things will begin to calm down as you realize that all food is available to you when ever you want. This part may seem a little scary to you at first, not trusting yourself, feeling out of control and thinking you will become huge. Again just try to be aware of what is happening, listen to your body and trust your intuition.

♦ Some people may begin to eat less at each meal without even realizing. This may be because you now consciously taste your food, and are listening to what your body needs and when your body has had enough.

♦ In the beginning you may be easily distracted by thoughts. When beginning any mindful practice this is completely normal and this happens to everyone throughout any mindful practice but rest assured your thoughts do become less and less as you become more focused and practiced.

♦ If you have family it may be difficult for you to eat without external distractions, perhaps you could ask them to join you eating in silence. If this doesn't work then perhaps waiting until your family have eaten and then eat alone or eat one course mindfully before your family join you.

♦ What you may notice after eating a meal mindfully is that you remain mindful for sometime after the meal. You may also notice that during other tasks throughout the day that you are beginning to be more mindful with other things.

♦ You may also find that you are more inclined to eat mindfully if you have prepared your meal mindfully.

ACTIVITY
Reflective Exercise

As you begin to adopt the practice of mindful eating you may notice that your choice of foods and how you prepare your meals begins to change. Think a little ahead, choose an evening you have some time and then buy what you would like to prepare and eat that evening. Do this mindfully really thinking about the food you are choosing, where it has come from, how it has been grown and buy organic if you can. When you are ready to make your meal, prepare the food mindfully. Cook each ingredient from start to finish, make your own sauce if you are having sauce, go out and pick some fresh herbs from the garden if you have them. Prepare and cook all the food you need for your meal from start to finish, no processed or ready prepared food should be used in this meal. Lay your table how you would like, make it inviting, use your best dishes, and make sure you won't be disturbed.

On a different evening when you have no time, you are rushing around your kids might be screaming and you are finding it difficult to do anything mindfully let alone eating. Perhaps you have an appointment to keep or you need to run your kids somewhere and you just cant seem to find enough hours in the day to do anything. If you are not used to preparing meals and usually eat ready prepared food then do as you would normally. Perhaps you already have a ready meal in your refrigerator. Then take it out and quickly zap it in the microwave, take it out the container if you want, or just eat it out the container it is already in, while you stand and watch TV or take a phone call not even thinking about what you are doing.

On each of the separate evenings you eat, note your entire experience. You can do this by writing down what was going on for you at the time, how you were feeling before, during and after eating the food, what you chose to eat, why you chose that particular food, what kind of hunger you were experiencing and where you were when you ate it. How much did you eat, did you eat more than usual or less. How did your body feel after every meal?

Then when you have all the information about each separate experience, sit down and take the time to read what you have written. See if there are any differences, ask yourself which meal you preferred and why. Try and understand what was going on for you at the time and why you ate the way you did and if experiencing a new way of eating makes you want to change anything.

CHAPTER 11

"Our bodies communicate to us clearly and specifically, if we are willing to listen to them"
(Shakti Gawain)

BODY TALK

Respect your body, you only get one. It is the vehicle that carries you through life and it is important to take care of it both on the inside and outside. Many of us are more inclined to focus on the outside, making ourselves look good and believing that what we can see is more important than what we cannot see. Caring for your body on the outside is important but just think for a moment of all the functions your body performs from within, without any conscious effort from your self. It breathes and it pumps blood round your whole body. From the minute you are born to the time of death your heart never stops beating. We cry, we laugh, we smile, we blink, we digest food and our body even tells us when something is not quite right or when we are sick, the list goes on. Do we always listen to what it communicates? Not really. So many of us take it for granted, and almost everyone at some time in their life will abuse their body in some way. The body really is quite an amazing machine that seems to keep going no matter how much we abuse or disrespect it. So perhaps we need to take some time out just to think about how well our body serves us and begin to treat it with much more respect, compassion and care. If you don't look after your body then who will?

Physical Activity

Regular physical activity at a moderate intensity can significantly improve our health and well-being and has been shown to increase energy, lower stress, increase restful sleep, improve bone strength, improve our resistance to illness, and improve health and well being generally. It can also increase awareness and acceptance of your body size and shape and increase your physical and emotional self-confidence. Physical activity is not just about the body. Your mind is the driving force behind any type of physical activity or exercise you take part in. In fact for anyone who has serious physical goals in mind, like running a marathon or becoming a professional tennis player, unless your mind is completely focused on achieving these goals, the chances are that you probably won't see much improvement.

Many of you will not be looking to run a marathon, become a professional tennis player or to get into any big, serious physical activity or exercise. Often we do not exercise because we have convinced ourselves that we don't have time. While many of us are very busy with our lives and families, it is still possible to incorporate some form of enjoyable physical activity into our lives. Time is not always the issue though. Some of us don't like to exercise because we find it boring or unpleasant. "Mindful Physical Activity" is different, as in mindful eating it is about getting in touch with your body and listening to what your body wants.

"Mindful Physical Activity" is something which commands much more than a few paragraphs. Taking on board mindful eating is one way of improving your relationship with food but many of you may find that as you embrace this new mind set you will begin to develop a whole new way of thinking and behaving. Your approach to different aspects of your life will automatically begin to change with little or no effort on your part. As you begin to understand the mind body connection and the importance of each and every aspect of our being, you may then ask yourself, what physical activity means to you?

Everybody is different and has different individual needs which are best met by following your intuition. Which ever form of physical activity or exercise you choose should be because you want to do it and you enjoy it. Following an exercise routine which is boring, time consuming and not enjoyable will achieve nothing. You will just become frustrated, fed-up, bored and give up. If your inner dialogue says "I must exercise this many days per week for this length of time" then you are not listening to your body but to the negative incessant mind chatter that you have become so used to through dieting. Ask yourself this, "What's your motivation?" If you find that the objective of any form of physical exercise or activity is based on the end result, such as losing weight, toning up, maintaining a strict weight management regime etc then don't waste your time. Always keep in mind that "Happiness is a journey, not a destination" Work like you don't need money, love like you've never been hurt and dance like no one's watching. The following suggestions will help you be more mindful as you choose what kind of physical activities you really enjoy!

- When your body is telling you something – listen!
- Exercise because you want to, not because you feel that you have to.
- Do exercise activities that you enjoy.
- Include lots of different activities.

- Get some physical activity every day, even if it is just a 10minute walk.
- Always drink plenty of water during exercise and afterwards.

Just remind yourself of what it was like when you embarked on a new diet. It is Monday morning and you are sitting in the kitchen having just denied yourself what you really want to eat for your breakfast but are determined to stick to your new diet. You begin writing out your daily/weekly plan of what you can and can't eat on this diet and promise yourself that you will go to the Gym every day, devising what exercise regime you are going to follow while promising yourself that you will run 3 miles every other day come rain, hail or shine.

That's not about listening to what your body really wants or needs, that's setting yourself up to fail even before you begin, it's about denial, rules, pain, discomfort, punishment etc. Mindful Physical Activity is no different to Mindful Eating in as much as you stop, breathe and listen to what your body needs. Why not begin by trying a variety of things you enjoy doing when your body feels up to doing them. Exercising for the right reasons will allow you to honour your intuitive sense and can lead to enjoyment, stress relief, and improved physical and emotional health.

There are a number of ways we can incorporate physical activity into our daily lives and incorporating mindfulness into the various activities you choose to do. Taking the stairs instead of the lift, getting off the bus one stop early and walking the last part, choosing to walk upstairs rather than take the lift, and parking your car in the furthest parking space from your office building are all means of "mindful physical activity."

Again as you begin to listen to your body you may find yourself wanting to be more active and take part in activities that involve being more physical than you are used to. We humans were never meant to live such sedentary lives. While exercising, whether this is walking, swimming, going to the gym or just taking the stairs instead of the lift, be in the moment and focus on how your body feels. Focus on the physical sensations you are feeling at that moment, does it feel good, is it hurting, are you feeling out of breath or are you relaxed? This is very important when it comes to deciding whether or not you are working towards your greatest potential.

Bear in mind that to reap the rewards of physical exercise adults should aim to take some form of exercise for at least 30 minutes on most days of the week. Taking 30 minutes of moderate physical activity on most days of the week will reduce your risk of chronic disease, but if you increase that to 60-90 minutes of moderate to vigorous physical activity, this will help sustain a healthy weight and maintain any weight loss.

The intensity at which you undertake any exercise is also important. An easy way to work out how hard you are working is by observing yourself as you exercise while having a conversation with someone. If you are able to hold a normal conversation you are working at a light intensity. If you are able to carry on a conversation with short breaks to catch your breath then you are working at a moderate intensity. If you need to slow down, stop or find yourself really out of breath and gasping for air as you carry on the conversation you are working at a high intensity. If you are being mindful as you do your activity just listen to what your body is saying and you will soon know how hard you need to work. Just take each day at a time, some days you may feel like taking in some hard strenuous activity and other days you may feel tired and lethargic. These are both ways in which your body is communicating with you, remember to listen!

TIPS

Here are a few tips on how to develop a more mindful practice towards physical activity:

- ◆ Remember to practice mindfulness as often as you can.

- ◆ Be kind to yourself and respect the internal messages you receive.

- ◆ Understand what motivates you to exercise and respond accordingly.

- ◆ Adjust your exercise as needed and develop the healthiest motives.

- ◆ Set aside the time your body and mind need to take care of your self.

- ◆ Never exercise because you should, this is not mindful

- ◆ Get rid of any thoughts about weight loss, calorie control or fat burning exercises (This is not what mindful physical activity is about)

ACTIVITY
Mindful Physical Exercise

Choose an exercise that you want to do and that you enjoy. At the beginning of the exercise make it your intention to be mindful throughout and observe everything. Notice every movement you make including your posture and breathing. If you usually go to the gym and run on a treadmill while listening to music, stop listening to the music or start running in an environment where there is no music playing. As you run begin by observing your self, the pace you are running, the rhythm, where your arms are, what your feet are doing, is everything in sync? Notice what it feels like when one foot touches the floor, when your weight shifts from one foot to another or when your foot lands on some uneven ground. Keep your focus just in front of you. Resist the temptation to look at your feet or pay attention to what's around you and do your best to remain focused on your running and nothing else. If any thoughts or feelings arise, notice them and then return your attention to running. Just focus on your body, nothing else. If it's cycling you enjoy, become aware of your legs as you push them round with each pedal action, notice how your neck and back feel. Do you feel relaxed and focused? If it's swimming you like, become aware of your arms as you lift them up out of the water and then plunge them back in. Observe each movement you body makes, your feet, your legs, your arms, head and so on.

The intention is just to observe, not be in the action or part of it but an observer watching a body running, cycling or swimming or whatever. In time you will find with most forms of repetitive exercise that eventually you begin to develop an awareness of the whole body. In the beginning you may find it hard not to listen to music or focus on your surroundings while running or doing a work out. As with all these activities, just take your time, don't force anything just intend to observe whatever is happening to your body throughout the exercise without criticism or judgment. Not only will you give your body a physical workout, but by being mindful as you do this gives your mind a workout too.

When you have completed the activity ask yourself the following questions. In what way was this different from your regular workout or exercise regime?

Is there a particular time during the day when you might be able to practice this? What kind of things got in the way of paying attention to your exercise?

CHAPTER 12

"Because you are in control of your life. Don't ever forget that. You are what you are because of the conscious and subconscious choices you have made" (Barbara Hall, 2000)

FREEDOM

So are you ready to change your relationship with food? The first step is having the desire and commitment to change and believing in yourself. Believing that you are worth it and that you can make the changes you want to make. If you long to be able to eat without restriction, without the feeling of guilt and shame, if you long to be able to get back to "normal" eating, eating what you want, when you want and eating until you feel physically satisfied and full. If this is something you really long for, and never ever want to follow another diet again, then let's get started.

Just think there are no rules, there are no restrictions you can eat anything at any time without judgement or criticism. How different your life will be, you are finally free. Free to eat how ever you want. You never have to waken up on a Monday morning again and think" Oh no! Which diet am I starting today" "What am I allowed to eat today" No, you are finally free, free to choose when you eat, what you eat, how you eat and where you eat. When you begin, start small, set your intentions for each day and give it your best shot. Whether you decide to eat one thing mindfully that day, or you decide to stop watching TV with your evening meal. It doesn't matter just begin with whatever you feel comfortable with. If you achieve your intention for that day, then praise yourself. If you don't manage then don't give yourself a hard time, there will be plenty of other opportunities. Remember just noticing if you achieve your intention for that day or not is progress. If you think it would be easier to do it with someone then do it with a friend. Anyone can learn to eat mindfully.

You are not only free to eat exactly how you want but you are also free to choose what clothes you wear and you are finally free to be yourself no matter what size or shape you are. What a great life, understanding, loving and accepting you for you. All you have do is take a moment to stop and listen to what your body is telling you...not your mind, just stop and listen! How easy could it be, what are you waiting for? Enjoy your life you are now free to choose how ever you want to live it!

MY STORY.......NOW

By addressing my issues in a number of different ways, I finally understood the connection and what I had to do to release myself from the undeniable effects of suppressing and denying my feelings over the course of my lifetime. This was achieved by using different complementary health methods, attending counselling, using different healing and energy modalities, becoming a complementary health practitioner myself, reading numerous self development books and by fully understanding and appreciating   the profound connection between mind and body.

What has now become crystal clear to me is that I have caused everything, with my negative thoughts and beliefs about myself. I felt very low on many occasions but now believe all my experiences have been essential to my personal development and have provided me with the necessary building blocks to where I find myself today. I am so grateful that I have had all these different opportunities and experiences which have brought me to this point in my life today. I now understand why everything has turned out this way.

It has allowed me to share my story and experiences with others, and how I have come to understand and accept that all my experiences and ways of coping were really important and necessary for me at that time. They have helped me uncover the many suppressed and denied feelings I have held on to throughout my life and have also helped me uncover the many negative beliefs I developed about myself over the years. Something I did because it felt safer to deny my true self than to risk the possibility of judgement, rejection or humiliation for being me and expressing how I felt.

Now I am much kinder to myself, I am beginning to love and accept myself completely and it is only through doing this that others will begin to accept me just as I am. I am no longer afraid to speak my truth and say what I feel. Some people will like me, some people will not but what's really important here is not what others think or believe about me but what I truly think and believe about me. I now know and understand that whatever I project outwards towards others is now consistent with what I want to see in my life and in the world around me. There is a very well known saying "You cannot truly love another until you truly love yourself"

The energy I have used over the years to keep me safe from the pain of rejection and disapproval, I am now using to help and encourage others to transform their lives. Writing this book in many ways has allowed me to purge myself of all the negativity and fear that paralyzed me and ultimately made my life what it was. I believe all of us can have and be exactly what we want, all we need to do is believe it and then act on that belief. Every one of us has the power and ability to bring about lasting change to our lives. I am passionate about self development and I am always available to support and help anyone on their own personal journey through my workshops or in one-to one consultation.

ADDITIONAL INFORMATION

As you become more accustomed to mindful eating your palate may well change and foods you may have liked or craved in the past will slowly become less palatable, perhaps tasting too sweet or too salty. The "Healthy Eating" information provided here is what is presently recommended but as you practice mindful eating your body will begin to tell you whether something is too salty or too sweet and exactly what your body needs.

The only reason various exercises, techniques, charts, tables and healthy eating information is included is for you to use initially to help you get in touch with your senses and become aware of your thoughts and actions. Some of these exercises, techniques etc you may enjoy using and find beneficial, others you may find are not for you and choose not to use them. It is important to use something that works for you and that you are comfortable with, at least give each one a shot. "If you do what you have always done, you will get what you have always got"…expansion is the great creator of abundance.

Healthy Eating

Healthy eating is about getting the balance right. A healthy and well balanced diet is the body's primary energy source. It constitutes the main building blocks for health and well being and aids in self healing and regeneration within the body. A well balanced diet will provide the body with all the essential nutrients it needs.

Shopping

Eating freshly prepared food is always a better option than ready made meals. It means that you are in control of how you prepare your own food and you know exactly what has gone into it. You will also be able to adjust the seasoning and anything extra you wish to add such as sugar or fat. If you do eat ready made meals or convenience foods then always read and check labels. Understanding food labels will help you make better choices. The ingredients on labels are always listed in descending order of weight. Always check the amount of fat and what quantity of fat are saturates. Less saturates are better. Also check sugar and salt content. The following is a guide which will help you decide whether a certain food is well balanced or not.

Please note the majority of food labels show the sodium content rather than salt. To convert sodium to salt you need to multiply the amount of sodium by 2.5g. One gram of sodium is the equivalent of 2.5g of salt.

Per 100g for complete main meal **A lot**....is this amount or more	Per 100g for complete main meal **A little**....is this amount or more
10g of sugars	2g of sugars
20g of fat	3g of fat
5g of saturates	1g of saturates
3g of fibre	0.5g of fibre
0.5 of sodium	0.1g sodium

The 5 Food Groups

The following pie chart shows the recommended proportions of food to eat from each of the 5 food groups. If you really do not have any idea at all what a balanced healthy diet looks like then this may help you initially when preparing meals and shopping. If you have become accustomed to eating lots of ready made meals, take away food and fast foods then it can be difficult to know just what balance you have. This is more or less what each meal should look like.

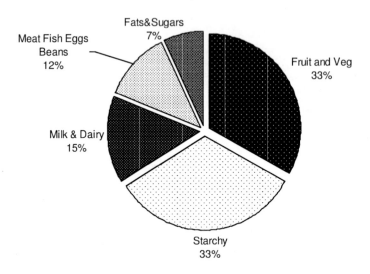

Bread Cereals and Potatoes

From the chart above you are able to see what the balance of a healthy meal should look like. More than 50% should consist of fruit and vegetables and starchy foods like, rice, potatoes, bread and cereals. If you base your meals on these kinds of foods you will feel fuller and more satisfied for longer. Often people think that the starchy foods are the ones to eat less of but starchy foods are the fillers and if you keep to the wholegrain types like brown rice, whole wheat pasta etc then they will keep you feeling fuller and more satisfied for longer. The mistake people often make is to add lots of fat like butter or cheese to these foods which then does make them a high fat food. Included in the starchy foods would be rice, pasta, bread, lentils, beans, potatoes, chapattis, oats and other dishes made from maize, cornmeal, millet, quinoa,

Your diet should include 4 to 6 portions of these foods per day. A portion would be an egg sized potato, 2 tablespoons of cooked rice/pasta/noodles or 3 tablespoons of breakfast cereals.

Fruit and Vegetables

Many of us don't eat the recommended minimum of 5 portions of fruit and/or vegetables a day. Instead of snacking on fruit which is probably the best way to eat fruit, as it only takes 30 minutes to digest and is better eaten alone. We often find ourselves eating a chocolate bar instead. People often get confused with portion sizes and what a portion actually is. A portion of fruit or vegetables is:

- A handful or grapes or strawberries or any berries
- 3 heaped tablespoons of cooked vegetables
- 1 piece of fruit such as an apple, banana, orange

Just drinking only fruit or vegetable juice is fine as it is packed full of nutrients but remember when the juice is made the pulp is lost which is important dietry fibre and can also help control hunger. Potatoes do not count as one of the 5 a day vegetables as they are too starchy and beans, pulses and dried fruits are only to be included once per day as they are also very starchy and sugary.

Milk and Dairy Foods

Milk, cheese, yoghurt, fromage frais are an important part of our diet as they provide most of the calcium we need and are also a good source of protein, minerals and vitamins and should be eaten in moderate amounts. Choosing the lower fat options are better for general healthy eating.

Your diet should include 2 to 3 portions per day. This should be roughly 1/6 of your total intake. A portion would be 200mls of milk, 150 g pot of yoghurt and 1oz (25g) of hard cheese such as cheddar.

Lean Meat, Poultry, Fish and Alternatives

Again only moderate amounts of this group are needed which also include, lentils, nuts, seeds, beans and eggs. Vegetarians can take a mixture of alternatives to make up the necessary amount of daily protein required. Fish is a good source of protein and the more oily fish like mackerel, salmon, sardines etc are a great source of Omega 3 oils which can often be lacking in our diets. Aim to eat at least 2 portions of fish per week, one being from the oily fish. Be careful when eating red and fattier meats like beef or salami, these can be high fat choices and also high in saturated fats.

A portion would be 4 oz of lean red meat or poultry, 6 oz of white fish, 2 oz of oily fish or 3 tablespoons of beans or pulses.

Fatty and Sugary Foods

These foods also include any sugary drinks which so many people drink today. High fat foods should be eaten sparingly and sugary drinks should be taken less frequently than most people take them. Fatty foods would include, butter, cream, cooking oils, margarine, crisps, cakes, pastries, mayonnaise, chocolate and any other sugary sweets or drinks. These foods should make up less than 1/12 of your total intake.

If you are used to snacking all the time and not eating regular meals it might be best to start with eating at least one proper meal a day with a balance of carbohydrates, lean protein, and healthy fat in this meal. When you are buying food always get the best quality version of that food that you can afford and if you can buy organic then do. Make this one meal special and follow the process for your first mindful meal taking the time to prepare the food mindfully and set the table perhaps placing a few fresh flowers out the garden on the table and using your favourite dinner plates to set the table and help generate a gentle and relaxing atmosphere.

Water

There are a number of different theories and suggestions relating to the amount of water our bodies require in order that they remain healthy and hydrated. The amount of water each of us requires on a daily basis varies and is dependent on where you live, how active you are and how your health is. Some of the problems associated with lack of fluids can cause bad breath, headaches, fatigue, lethargy, constipation etc

Health Benefits of Water

The body is made up of 60% water and is essential for each system and organ within the body to function correctly. Water is lost through our breath, perspiration, urine and bowel movements. The water that is lost in our bodies must be replenished by eating and drinking adequate amounts. There are a number of different suggestions on how to keep the body continually hydrated. Some say we should be drinking 2litres of water daily not including drinks such as tea, coffee, etc which can be considered dehydrating, while others say we need 2litres of fluid daily which includes things like tea, coffee, juice, water etc, others suggest that it should be more than this and men need more fluid than women. So opinions really do vary on this and for peace of mind apart from the above suggestions, if you drink enough fluid throughout the day so that you very seldom feel thirsty and your urine is more or less colourless, slightly yellow then your fluid intake is probably adequate.

FEELINGS BUBBLES

How we might feel when our needs are not being met

troubled   upset   ashamed   embarrassed   deprived
guilty   tired   sleepy   exhausted   grief   hurt   lonely   sad
miserable   depressed   shaky   unhappy   hopeless   upset
disappointed   withdrawn   irritable   restless   dejected
disheartened   stressed   guarded   helpless   despair
discouraged   fragile   insecure   sensitive   jealous   shaky
longing   frustrated   angry   resentful

How we might feel when our needs are being met

Warm   tender   confident   safe   secure   stimulated   inspired
excited   happy   content   loving   giving   enthusiastic
energetic   passionate   grateful   appreciative   grateful
hopeful   optimistic   encouraged   peaceful   calm   fulfilled
relaxed   trusting   satisfied   vibrant   energetic   positive
delighted   thrilled   strong   capable   assertive   courageous

Feelings Journal

Strength of feeling on a scale of 0-10   0 = Mild   10 = Very Strong

Date............

Time day/night	What do I feel?	What is happening right now?	How strong is the feeling?	How long did the feeling last?	Did I eat to cope with the feeling?	What did I eat and how much?	How do I feel after eating it?

Daily Eating Journal

Date..................

Strength of feeling on a scale of 0-10   0 = Mild   10 = Very Strong

Meal	Hunger Score	How do I feel? Note strength of emotion and how long it lasted.	Why do I want to eat?	When do I eat?	Where am I when I want to eat? Home, out, driving etc	How do I eat? Fast, slow, in secret etc	What do I want to eat? Note what you eat and how much.
Breakfast							
Snack							
Lunch							
Snack							
Dinner							
Snack							

134

RECOMMENDED READING

Susan Albers, **Eating Mindfully,** New Herbinger Publications, 2003

Jan Chozen Bays, **Mindful Eating,** Shambhala, 2009

Anthony Demello, **Awareness,** Harper Collins, 1997

Wayne Dyer, **The Power of Intention,** Hay House, 2004

Wayne Dyer, **Change your Thoughts, Change your Life,** Hay House, 2008

Christopher K. Germer, **The Mindful Path to Self-Compassion,** The Guildford Press, 2009

David Hamilton, **It's the Thought That Counts,** Hay House, 2005

David Hamilton, **Destiny V's Free Will,** Hay House, 2007

Valerie and Paul Lynch, **Emotional Healing in Minutes,** Thorsons, 2001

Andreas Moritz, **Freedom from Judgment,** Freedom from Judgment, 2001, 2002

Silva Nakkach & Gael Chiarella, **Conscious Eating,** Relaxation Company, 2005

Oriah Mountain Dreamer, **The Invitation,** Thorsons, 2000

Oriah Mountain Dreamer, **The Dance,** Thorsons, 2001

Ekhart Tolle, **A New Earth,** penguin Books Ltd, 2005

Stuarte Wilde, **Weight Loss for the Mind,** Hay House Inc, 2005

Stuarte Wilde, **Silent Power,** Hay House Inc, 2006

Perry Wood, **The Secrets of the People Whisperer,** 2004, Rider

Research Article American Journal of Health Education May/June 2006, Volume 37, No 3

RESOURCES and WEBSITES

Many of the following resources I have personally used myself and others I have either worked with or know personally and respect and recommend the services they offer.

Dr David Hamilton, PhD is based in Glasgow where he previously worked as a scientist in the pharmaceutical industry. He is now a Hay House published author and has written a number of thought provoking books on the nature of the mind-body connection. David believes that we as individuals intuitively know how to heal ourselves and brings together the research of many scientific experiments to support this. David currently gives talks and runs workshops in the UK and around the world.
Website address: www.drdavidhamilton.com

Bio-energy Therapy Bitney MacNab, my sister works as a Bio-energy Therapist and runs a thriving practice in the heart of Perthshire. Bio-energy clears blockages in people's energy fields. Once the flow is restored the body can get on with the process of returning to full health. A course of at least 4 sessions is recommended to allow imbalances to be cleared but as everyone is different, some may require more sessions. Throughout the treatment you will be encouraged to participate in your own recovery by learning that our health is affected by how we think and how this can be changed. If you choose to use the Domancic method (there are a number of different methods that can be used) to address your ailments you will most likely find it a powerful tool to access the unconscious to allow old belief systems to be released. As a practitioner Bitney has absolute faith in bio-energy healing to allow each individual to be in the fullest of health possible.

Website address: www.bioenergyshifts.weebly.com

Hypnotherapy Kay Strang is a practising clinical Hypnotherapist, EFT practitioner and NLP practitioner and runs a busy and successful practice in Perthshire. She is available for individual consultations and can offer help with smoking, weight, anxiety, depression, phobias and emotional problems. Her Telephone number is: 01877 339477

Website address: www.kaystranghypnotherapy.co.uk

Yoga and Counselling Lucille Henderson is a trained counsellor, supervisor and trainer and has specialised in relationship counselling for the past twenty years. She has a keen interest in the interconnectedness of body, mind and spirit and the impact feelings have on the body. She teaches a gentle flowing form of Yoga that connects to the inner rhythms of the body, creating inner peace and awareness.

E-Mail address: lucille@luedon.plus.com

Photography Ken Paterson has worked as a commercial photographer in Scotland for the last twenty years. While working as a lecturer in photography at Stevenson College he is pursuing his own project to create a series of photographic essays on historical Famous Scots from around the world. This project is based on his belief that the strength of a nation lies within its sense of community, the heart of a nation within its people, and the soul of a nation within its history.

Website address www.kenpaterson.co.uk

Workplace Health and Well-Being Services provided by Peace of Mind help businesses and organizations to improve productivity while keeping costs down. Many of the most forward thinking, proactive companies today recognize that work related stress, sickness and absenteeism are the main barriers to an effective and productive workforce. The following services provided by Peace of Mind include:

Staff Training Workshops and Seminars
One-to-One Consultations
Health Checks
Health events and Fairs
Quiet Room Consultancy Services
Website address: www.peaceofmindscotland.co.uk

Quiet Room Consultancy Services was established in 2007 by Jeni MacNab. The concept of a Quiet Room was first developed for primary schools in Merseyside. This involved developing an environment that was both relaxing and health promoting to help young people who were experiencing emotional and behavioural problems. Through Jeni's vision and determination back in 2005 she further developed this idea. Quiet Room Consultancy Services now offers anyone in any type of organization or home the opportunity to experience the health promoting benefits of having a Quiet Room.
Website Address: www.quietroomconsultancyservices.co.uk

EFT Emotional Freedom Technique EFT is a psychological version of acupressure. The technique involves gently tapping a sequence of energy points on the body with the fingertips, which releases the negative emotion.

This is a technique that can be mastered easily by anyone and can be used effectively without the need for a therapist. Stress, anxiety, fears, phobias, eating disorders, addictions and many more issues can be successfully treated using this treatment. To learn more about this technique and the founder Gary Craig please visit the website below.

Website Address: www.emofree.com

Other Useful Resources and Sites

National Centre for Eating Disorders www.eating-disorders-org.uk

Confederation of Scottish Counselling Agencies www.cosca.org.uk

British Association for Counselling and Psychotherapy www.bacp.co.uk

For information on workshops or one-to-one consultations offered by Jeni contact: jeni@peaceofmindscotland.com